Contents

Tables and figures

Summary

Chapter 1

1.1 Recent health policy in the UK has focused on the role of health promotion as a strategy for the dual aims of disease prevention and to improve the overall health status of the population.

1.2 There has been no systematic attempt to develop a framework for the practical evaluation of the cost-effectiveness of alternative health promotion and disease prevention initiatives. This is the main objective of this report.

Chapter 2

2.1 Cost-effectiveness analysis can be used either to identify the intervention which achieves a specific target at lowest cost or that which achieves the greatest outcome for a given cost.

2.2 An example is provided in this section of the costs per quitter and the costs per life year saved for a national no-smoking day compared to a national mass media campaign.

2.3 The economic evaluation framework for assessing the cost-effectiveness of health promotion has six stages – definition of the study problem; setting of economic objectives; consideration of options; study design; costs and outcomes; the production of final cost per unit of outcome measures.

2.4 These stages can be represented as questions. Examples of questions posed for the economic evaluation of health education are presented in this section.

Chapter 3

3.1 In defining the study problem two main issues exist – to determine the scope of the evaluation and to identify the perspective to be adopted. Setting economic objectives involves converting general aims for health promotion into cost per unit of outcome objectives.

3.2 For the study problem, four levels for assessing the cost-effectiveness of health promotion activities are defined dependent on the scope and perspective of the study. Using health education as a reference intervention, level 1 type analysis is an assessment of the cost-effectiveness of alternative health education activities, level 2 assesses the cost-effectiveness of health education compared with alternative health promotion or prevention interventions, level 3 examines the cost-effectiveness of health education compared with treatment and curative options whilst level 4 assesses health education compared with other uses of public resources (e.g. defence, transport). The perspective adopted can be single agency, multi-agency or society.

3.3 The two general aims of health promotion are the prevention of ill-health and the promotion of good health or well-being. Economic objectives are defined more specifically as the achievement of 'lowest costs per unit of outcome' or 'greatest outcomes per unit of cost'. These represent efficiency objectives although equity objectives can also be incorporated e.g. 'lowest cost per unit of outcome for unemployed individuals'.

Chapter 4

4.1 Option choice in an economic evaluation of health promotion is influenced by the dimensions and definitions of health promotion, the scope of the study, the perspective and the number of options. A classification of health promotion options can be developed, but requires a three-stage process: defining the dimensions of alternative health education, health protection and prevention measures; the use of a model of health promotion for devising an option choice framework; the production of a final health promotion option schema suitable for cost-effectiveness analysis.

4.2 This section outlines recent thinking among health promotion experts of the definition and scope of health education, health protection and disease prevention measures. For example, a new approach to health education is the notion of its role for political and social awareness raising and for self-empowerment. Health protection covers interventions that attempt to influence social, economic and environmental change in a way that is beneficial to health but are normally considered to be outside of the direct control of each individual it affects (e.g. water fluoridation). Prevention can be primary (e.g. immunization), secondary (e.g. screening) or tertiary (e.g. control of disease) but choice of whether or not to receive it is controlled to a greater extent by each individual.

4.3 Tannahill (1985) has produced a model of health promotion which illustrates the linkages between health education, health protection and prevention. By using three overlapping circles to represent seven domains of health promotion, this model can be used to classify a range of option types for an economic evaluation. An updated version is used in this report (Downie, Fyfe and Tannahill 1991).

4.4 Three further steps are outlined using Tannahill's model to generate health promotion options for economic evaluation. Firstly, the supply (provision/delivery) and demand (coverage/uptake) processes of the domains of Tannahill's model can be determined. Secondly, the domains of Tannahill's model are fitted into the supply-demand process dimensions. Thirdly, the options for an economic evaluation are defined. This approach enables a large degree of specificity to be achieved in describing options.

4.5 A further stage is to examine the processes involved in defining any one option, for example, health education. This involves determining the setting/channel for health education, a risk factor strategy (e.g. single- or multi-risk factor) and broad objective of the option (e.g. disease prevention, quality of life gains). A framework of specific health education options is provided in this section. In addition, a choice exists between a high risk group strategy and a population based approach. The choice could be incorporated into an evaluation as two separate options for health education.

Chapter 5

5.1 The establishment of the efficiency of a health promotion intervention (i.e. cost-effectiveness) requires that evidence is generated of both the efficacy (i.e. whether it works in ideal study conditions) and effectiveness (whether it improves outcomes in actual settings) of the intervention.

5.2 In an economic evaluation the construction of a rigorous and reliable study design is very important to enable the assignment of specific outcomes to different interventions. There are three broad types of study design that have been used in the evaluation of this relationship for health promotion and prevention interventions: experimental, quasi-experimental and non-experimental. These are described in this section.

5.3 Experimental study designs generally achieve greater internal validity (i.e. the extent to which changes in outcome can be attributed to the inputs of the intervention), but have lower external validity (i.e. evidence of effectiveness in actual settings). External validity can be better achieved using quasi-experimental designs although at a cost of lower internal validity. The problem for health promotion evaluation is to achieve an even balance between internal and external validity.

Chapter 6

6.1 Cost in an economic evaluation is defined as the value of using resources in a specified health promotion programme rather than in an alternative use (the notion of opportunity cost).

6.2 The measurement of costs involves assessment of the type of costs included (e.g. direct costs to the provider agencies, costs of time and money incurred by individuals receiving health education), the collection of data on resource use and the valuation of resources used in a health promotion option.

Chapter 7

7.1 An appropriate outcome measure is required in order to compare the cost-effectiveness of alternative options. There are three interrelated types of outcome measure that can be used – process indicators, intermediate outcomes and final outcomes.

7.2 This section provides a description of the use of each of the three types of outcome measure:
(a) *Process indicators* provide a quantitative measure of health promotion service delivery effectiveness. They are programme-specific measures and so cannot be used to directly compare outcomes from different types of health promotion programme. A distinction can be made between the supply and demand dimensions of these indicators. Examples are provided in this section.

(b) *Intermediate outcomes* represent the middle stage between the provision and uptake of health promotion and impact on final health outcomes. The appropriate type of intermediate outcome to use varies according to the type of options in the evaluation. In many cases health behaviour modification (e.g. reduction in smoking prevalence) represents an appropriate outcome measure. Health behaviour change may be achieved through individual choice or through formal group agreement, regulation or coercion (e.g. no-smoking policies, seatbelt legislation). Some prevention activities such as immunization have no intermediate outcome measure, whilst community development initiatives may use a measure of change in 'informed health choices'.

(c) *Final health outcomes* measure changes in health status. There are several types which vary in the extent to which they attempt to provide a general measure of health. Measures such as the quality adjusted life year and quality of well-being scale, are derived from single numerical scales of health incorporating physical, mental and social functioning dimensions. Less comprehensive, but conceptually simpler are measures of health outcome such as 'disability-free life expectancy'. Most basic are the single dimension measures such as life years saved. A further choice exists between the use of disease specific health measures or general health status indices such as those outlined above.

7.3 The appropriate outcome measure for comparisons between alternative health promotion options depends on the objective and scope of the evaluation and the aims of the objectives included in the analysis. For example, two smoking cessation options may have different practical objectives which means using an intermediate outcome measure to compare them, such as changes in smoking prevalence, is inappropriate.

7.4 In order to enhance the comparability of results from economic evaluations of health promotion programmes, use should be made of health status measures such as quality adjusted life years. However, there is no 'best method' for measuring changes in quality of life due to health promotion, although several instruments exist.

The direct measurement of the effectiveness of a health promotion intervention using final outcomes can be a costly and time-consuming exercise, requiring a prospective study following a cohort of individuals over time. A more pragmatic and less costly approach is to measure intermediate outcomes and predict final health outcomes using available epidemiological evidence (or epidemiological models such as PREVENT). Several difficulties with this approach are outlined in this section.

A trade-off exists between the cost of evaluation and the scope and reliability of final health outcomes.

7.5 There is a need in economic evaluations of health promotion programmes in actual settings to consider the possible cumulative impact of such programmes on outcomes of overtime and across interventions.

Chapter 8

8.1 Three progressively more detailed approaches to the presentation of cost-effectiveness results are: (a) the production of baseline average costs per unit of outcome, (b) the assessment of additional costs per extra unit of outcome for an expansion (or contraction) of health promotion options and (c) the modification of baseline cost per unit of outcome results to allow for differences in the timing of costs and outcomes, uncertainty regarding the reliability of cost and outcome estimates and the inclusion of equity objectives.

8.2 The production of baseline average costs per unit of outcome represents the 'best estimate' given the data available, the assumptions used to derive costs and outcomes and the judgement of the analyst. Net costs could be used by incorporating an estimate of potential savings to society from reduced health care costs, or increased work production, due to health promotion.

8.3 A debate among economists is whether or not health promotion and prevention actually save future health care resources and produces other cost savings for society. The actual impact is uncertain but is important for the production of net cost per unit of outcome results.

8.4 Often the decision maker is faced with a judgement of how to allocate resources efficiently between existing health promotion programmes. The production of estimates of the additional costs of extra outcomes from expanding different interventions (or vice versa for contracting interventions) can assist in this decision making process. This approach, known as the evaluation of marginal cost-effectiveness, is particularly important for evaluating multi-component community health promotion programmes.

8.5 A basic behavioural principle used in economic analysis is that people or agencies prefer to delay costs but to obtain immediate benefits. This suggests a lower valuation for the health benefits of health promotion and prevention that occur in the future. A current debate among economists is whether future health benefits should be valued at the same rate as current benefits, an action which would improve the relative cost-effectiveness of prevention compared to treatment interventions.

8.6 The issue of equity has been given little attention in previous economic evaluations of preventive and health promotion programmes. The notion of equity is multi-faceted (e.g. equity of access, equity of health). For the purposes of an economic evaluation, equity objectives need to be clearly defined. It is appropriate for an evaluation of a health promotion programme to have as its starting point a pre-defined equity objective such as improving the diet of communities living in socially deprived areas, and then determine the most cost-effective dietary health education strategy for meeting targets related to this objective.

Chapter 9

9.1 The economic evaluation framework developed in chapters 2 to 8 has two main applications:
(a) *Retrospective*, as a framework to assess the content and quality of previous studies of the cost-effectiveness of health promotion.
(b) *Prospective*, to provide guidelines for the development of actual evaluations of the cost-effectiveness of health promotion interventions.

In this chapter the use of the framework for the first of these applications above is outlined. Three areas of health promotion activity were selected as case studies: exercise/diet interventions, smoking cessation health education and workplace health promotion. A number of published studies for each case study area are reviewed.

In addition, the studies are assessed according to scope, generalizability and comparability of results criteria.

9.2 This section reviews three diet/exercise cost-effectiveness evaluations.

9.3 This section reviews three studies of the cost-effectiveness of smoking cessation health education.

9.4 This section reviews the general quality of the economic evaluations of workplace health promotion programmes.

The aim of the case studies is to demonstrate to health promotionalists and other non-economists the possibilities of using the economic evaluation framework to assess published studies which claim to examine the cost-effectiveness of health promotion.

Chapter 10

The next stage in the development of the economic evaluation framework is to apply it to the assessment of the cost-effectiveness of actual health promotion and health education interventions.

1 The health promotion policy context for economic evaluation

1.1 Health promotion and public health policy

Until the 1970s the main role of the health service in the UK was as a provider of medical care. Following the reorganization of the National Health Service in 1973, health service providers, in collaboration with other community services had an important role in the prevention of disease. Subsequently, several national strategy documents were produced by the government which have placed the prevention of disease as a high priority in public health policy (Department of Health and Social Security 1977, 1979). There is now a growing body of epidemiological knowledge linking the growth in incidence of chronic diseases, such as coronary heart disease and cancers, with lifestyle factors such as smoking and diet, and socio-economic and environmental determinants, for example, social class and poverty.

More recently, health policy in the UK has focused on the role of health promotion as a strategy for the dual aims of disease prevention and to improve the overall health status of the population. National health promotion strategies have been produced separately by Wales in 1990 (Health Promotion Authority for Wales, 1990), Scotland in 1991 (Scottish Home and Health Department, 1991) and England in 1992 (Department of Health, 1992). In each strategy there is a recognition that the social and physical environment in which people live affects their choices regarding healthy behaviour. An interest in the health of the general population has been the guiding philosophy behind specific sections of the recent health service reforms in the UK. For example, the new General Practitioner (GP) contract states that the responsibility of family doctors is for the health of all those registered with their practices and not just those needing medical treatment. The main instruments for this are the three-yearly health checks, health promotion clinics, incentive payments to meet immunization targets and specific screening activities.

1.2 The role of economic evaluation

The government strategy document on health promotion produced for England – *The Health of the Nation* – states that resources for health promotion and disease prevention should be concentrated on areas where action is most likely to be effective (Department of Health, 1991, 1992). This implies an important role for economic evaluation to determine cost-effective interventions for disease prevention and health status improvements. Despite this assertion cost-effectiveness and equity criteria were not used in the planning and selection of *Health of the Nation* target areas (Akehurst *et al.* 1991). This may be due to a lack of empirical evidence (especially in the UK) or from a lack of

1

an appropriate model for evaluating the cost-effectiveness of health promotion.

There have been several attempts to apply economic theory and economic appraisal to identify the potential impacts of health promotion and prevention (Engleman and Forbes 1986, Cohen and Henderson, 1988). However, there has been no attempt to systematically develop a framework for the practical evaluation of the cost-effectiveness of alternative health promotion and disease prevention initiatives. This is the main objective of this report.

In chapter 2 an overview of the economic evaluation framework is provided and chapters 3 to 8 discuss the main issues and practical problems associated with using the framework for analysis of the cost-effectiveness of health promotion. Each chapter focuses on a separate component of the framework. The use of the framework to assess the content and quality of published studies in this area is demonstrated in chapter 9. Several health promotion case studies are given as examples, covering exercise/diet, smoking and workplace interventions.

2 Using an economic evaluation framework

2.1 The purpose of cost-effectiveness analysis in health promotion

The main purpose of an economic evaluation is to assess how efficiently resources are being used in the pursuit of an objective or set of objectives. Efficiency in health promotion can be achieved by adopting a programme that provides the greatest outcome at the least cost. Cost-effectiveness analysis provides a method that can be used to determine the costs and outcomes of alternative interventions in order to assist the efficient use of resources. This analysis can either be used to identify the intervention which achieves a specific quantitative target at lowest cost or that which achieves the greatest outcome for a given cost. Managers are likely to want to know what is the most cost-effective use of resources for a range of alternative health promotion interventions, or whether resources can be more cost-effectively used by expanding or contracting different health promotion programmes.

2.2 The application of cost-effectiveness analysis – an example

A government sponsored health promotion agency might wish to compare the value for money of a national no-smoking day, consisting of an intensive one-day media and local events/activities campaign, with other options such as a national mass media campaign covering a defined period of time. One objective could be to assess which intervention achieved the lowest cost per quitter. For example, the UK national 'No-Smoking Day' has been estimated to achieve a permanent quit rate of 0.5% of all adult smokers or 50,000 people per annum at an approximate annual cost of £1 million incurred by the national organizing committee and participating district health authorities (Reid *et al.*, 1992). This produces an estimated cost of £20 per quitter (1992 prices). Reid *et al.* (1992) using published data estimated that a national mass media campaign would incur a total cost of £10 million and result in 750,000 quitters after a few months (this was based on the assumption of a higher quit rate of 5% of all adult smokers), producing a cost per quitter of approximately £13.

An alternative economic objective could be to compare the costs per life years saved for each intervention. Reid and Smith (1990) have estimated that a quit rate of 0.5% of all adult smokers from a no-smoking day could result in a total of 107,500 life years saved, compared to two million life years saved from a longer-scale national mass media campaign (assuming a higher quit rate of 5% of all smokers). This produces a cost per life year saved of £9.30 for the no-smoking day and £5 for the mass media intervention.

Although these are crude calculations, it appears that on the basis of both quitter and life years saved outcome measures, the no-smoking day is less cost-effective than the national mass media campaign. However, for health promotion managers with cash limited budgets this evidence may not provide much useful guidance for decision making. The additional benefits of the mass media campaign can only be achieved at a higher total cost than a no-smoking day. Nonetheless, cost-effectiveness data can assist in decisions over whether a programme that costs more but produces more total gain is worth the extra resources.

The limitation of cost-effectiveness analysis is that it can only aid decision making – it cannot unambiguously state whether achieving a greater gain is worth the extra resources that might be required. This needs more sophisticated cost benefit analysis where the costs and benefits are valued in monetary terms and the project is deemed worthwhile if the net outcome is positive. In cost-effectiveness analysis the resource allocation decision depends on the criteria and judgement of the policy makers (e.g. the health promotion budget manager).

This can be demonstrated by using the no-smoking day and national mass media campaign example. The cost of achieving an extra 700,000 quitters through the mass media campaign is £9 million at an additional cost per quitter of £13. The additional 1,892,500 life years saved through the mass media campaign can be achieved at an additional cost of less than £5 per life year saved. If the health promotion manager had set a provisional target of achieving 750,000 quitters or two million life years saved (with no explicit cash limits) the decision then becomes whether it is worth paying an extra £13 per quitter or £5 per life year saved to achieve this.

This may lead on to consideration of the wider uses of these resources, for example, on dietary health promotion or to considering other smoking reduction strategies (Reid and Smith, 1990, also considered school health education, family doctor training and workplace smoking policies as alternative options. However no cost per life year saved estimates were calculated). If total resources of £3 million were available for smoking related health education, then the no-smoking day option would be the only one viable from the two options considered above.

In contrast, the no-smoking day and mass media campaign may be considered by managers as complementary rather than as alternatives. The problem here may be whether to allocate additional resources to a mass media campaign as a follow-up to a no-smoking day initiative. Assuming (for this example) that a smaller national campaign could be purchased for less than £10 million, and assuming no change in proportionate effectiveness, decision makers may wish to determine whether it is worth allocating say a further £2 million to a mass media campaign subsequent to no-smoking day to achieve an estimated additional 400,000 life years saved (i.e. at £5 per life year saved). To address this problem, the cost-effectiveness of allocating the additional funds to mass media should be compared with the cost-effectiveness of using the resources for alternative (smoking cessation) health education options.

Another strategy is to either expand or contract a programme. For example, in 1985 the Health Education Council in England increased its expenditure on advertising for that year's 'No-Smoking Day' in an attempt to increase public awareness of the event. However, as this appeared to have no effect on participation rates, it was concluded not to be a cost-effective use of resources (D. Reid, pers. comm., 1992).

The example described in this section, however, is very simplistic but it does illustrate the potential role of cost-effectiveness analysis for decisions on resource allocation. Key elements are that a common outcome measure is required to compare interventions and that this measure needs to be appropriate for the objectives and perspectives adopted in the evaluation. In a complete evaluation, factors such as the perspective of the evaluation, public and/or risk group compliance to health education, the timing of costs and benefits, difficulties of data collection and the costs of evaluation and the political and social acceptability of the health education interventions would need greater consideration.

2.3 The economic evaluation framework

There are several stages in the assessment of the cost-effectiveness of health promotion which are outlined in the economic evaluation framework presented in Figure 1. The end point of this process is the production of a range of comparable estimates of the costs and effects of alternative interventions.

The importance of careful planning is implicit in the framework. There are three stages prior to the collection and analysis of data; these cover the definition of the study problem (stage A), the setting of economic objectives (stage B) and consideration of the options for comparison (stage C). Data collection and evaluation is represented by the stages covering the choice of study design for measuring effectiveness (stage D), the assessment of costs and outcomes (stages E and F) and the production of final cost per unit of outcome measures (stage G).

2.4 Questions posed in an economic evaluation

In Figure 1 the stages A–G are interrelated, each being dependent on a prior stage that needs to be adequately addressed. Each stage can be posed as a question that has to be addressed in order to progress on to the next stage. These questions can be outlined in relation to the evaluation of health education:

1. *What is the study problem that policy makers wish to address and whose perspective is relevant?* For example, is the issue to determine the most cost-effective use of a health authority budget for smoking cessation health education or to examine the resource allocation priorities of a government between a national heart disease prevention programme, hypertension control programmes or an expansion of heart disease surgery facilities? Chapter 3 discusses more fully the definition of the study problem.
2. *What are the economic objectives of the policy makers?* For example, this might be to identify the lowest cost prevention option for reducing mortality from coronary heart disease, or to assess the expected

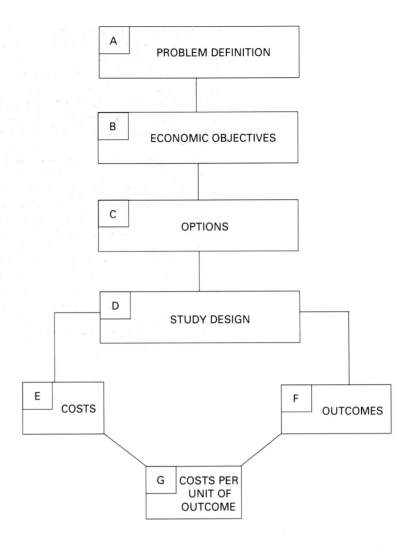

Figure 1. The basic economic evaluation framework.

additional costs and effects from using a new method of screening
people at risk of alcohol related problems. (See chapter 3.)

3. *What are the options to be included in an evaluation?* Examples of
possible options for the promotion of exercise could include a
national mass media campaign, a workplace initiative and school
health education which can be compared with a do-nothing
strategy (e.g. follow current practice). At this stage those options
which are not acceptable, those for political or ethical reasons, will
be identified and excluded from the data collection and analysis
stages (see chapter 4).

4. *What study design is appropriate for measuring the efficacy (i.e. does it
work) and effectiveness (how well does it work) of the options considered?*
There are several possible study designs for evaluating health

education which vary according to their statistical rigour and application to actual settings. Most rigour is obtained through an experimental study design whilst non-experimental and quasi-experimental designs enable a greater generalizability of the results to actual settings (see chapter 5).

5. *What are the costs and outcomes of the options considered?* Depending on the study problem and the economic objectives (stage A and B) the costs and appropriate outcome measures can be calculated. There are three levels of outcome measure – (1) process indicators, which are the most basic outcome measure (e.g. number of leaflets distributed, proportion of public aware of a mass media campaign); (2) intermediate outcomes (e.g. behaviourial change – smoking cessation, reduced salt intake in the diet, informed health choices) and (3) final outcomes, representing the top tier of measures (e.g. mortality, morbidity, quality adjusted life years) (chapter 6 examines costs and chapter 7 discusses outcomes.)

6. *How do the options compare in terms of their costs per unit of outcome?* Results are presented in order to address the initial objectives of the evaluation (stage B). The costs and outcomes calculated at stages E and F are combined. Adjustments can be made to the baseline result to allow for the differential timing of costs and outcomes, the imprecision of estimates and equity considerations (see chapter 8).

3 Defining the study problem and setting economic objectives

3.1 Overview

Before any actual data collection and analysis can begin for an economic evaluation of health promotion, the study problem has to be defined and the quantitative economic objectives need to be constructed. The two main issues in defining the study problem are: (a) to determine the scope of the evaluation and (b) the perspective to be adopted. The construction of economic objectives for the evaluation of health promotion involves the conversion of general descriptive aims into quantifiable cost per unit of outcome objectives. Figure 2 which develops stages A and B from Figure 1 summarizes these issues.

3.2 Problem definition

There are four main approaches to assessing the cost-effectiveness of health promotion activities, with each representing a level within a hierarchy of evaluations (Figure 2). The appropriate level to adopt will depend on the purpose of the evaluation.

Level 1. *What is the cost-effectiveness of alternative health education interventions?* For example, health promotion officers working for a district health authority might wish to examine the cost-effectiveness of their current practice of providing hospitals and clinics with leaflets on the health dangers of smoking compared to employing a specialist to provide health education to patients who smoke.

Level 2. *What is the cost-effectiveness of health education compared to alternative health promotion or prevention interventions?* For example, a national health promotion agency (e.g. the Health Education Authority) might wish to know the relative cost-effectiveness of a smoking cessation health education programme, a dietary health promotion campaign and health protection measures (e.g. water fluoridation, increases in tobacco taxation).

Level 3. *What is the cost-effectiveness of health education compared to treatment and curative interventions?* For instance, this might involve an evaluation comparing the use of diuretics or beta-blockers for the control of hypertension, surgery for heart disease and dietary health education.

Level 4. *What is the cost-effectiveness of health education compared to allocating additional resources to public sector services such as education or defence?* This is the broadest type of cost-effectiveness evaluation as it relates to the issue of how society's resources can best be allocated between different sectors to achieve the greatest overall benefit for society.

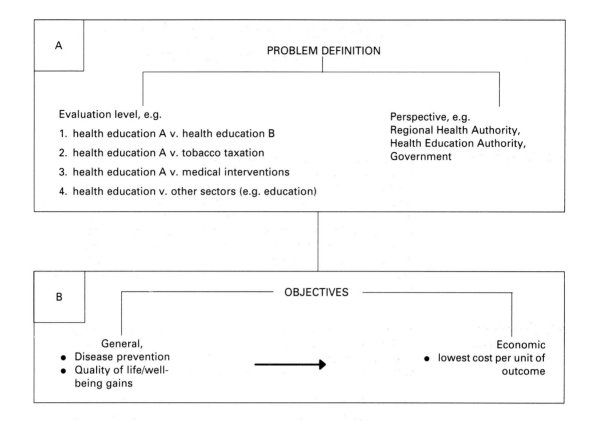

Figure 2. Problem definition and economic objectives.

These levels represent a progressive sequence for assessment of the cost-effectiveness of health education. Initially a level 1-type analysis might be conducted to determine the most cost-effective of, for example, several health education interventions for reducing the prevalence of smoking among teenagers. A level 2- or 3-type analysis could subsequently be conducted to address broader resource allocation choices by comparing the most cost-effective intervention from the level 1 analysis with other health promotion or treatment programmes.

However, it is the perspective of the evaluation that determines the scope of the economic evaluation. There are three broad perspectives that could be adopted at a local or national level.

A narrow perspective would be that of a single agency provider adopting a level 1-type evaluation. For example, the single agency could be a District Health Authority, a GP surgery, a workplace or, at the national level, the Health Education Authority (HEA).

A wider perspective involves assessing the costs and outcomes associated with a multi-agency health promotion programme and a level 2- or 3-type analysis. For example, a community based prevention programme could include inputs from District Health Authorities, Family Health Service Authorities, Social Service

Departments, voluntary agencies and the HEA.

The broadest perspective is that of society – this would involve consideration of the costs and outcomes of interventions affecting all relevant agencies, recipients of health promotion services/activities and other members of the public. This focus can be adopted for a level 1- or 2-type analysis but is essential for undertaking a level 3- or 4-type analysis.

Clarity in the perspective adopted is important for choosing the appropriate range of costs to include, and the outcome measures to use in an economic evaluation.

3.3 Economic objectives

Evaluation of the cost-effectiveness of health promotion and health education requires that general objectives are transformed into economic objectives (see stage B in Figure 2).

The UK Government's strategy document *The Health of the Nation* defines two general and interrelated objectives of health promotion – the prevention of ill health and the promotion of good health or well-being (Department of Health, 1992). Whereas the prevention of ill health aims to maintain health status and minimize any reduction over an individual's lifetime, the promotion of good health or well-

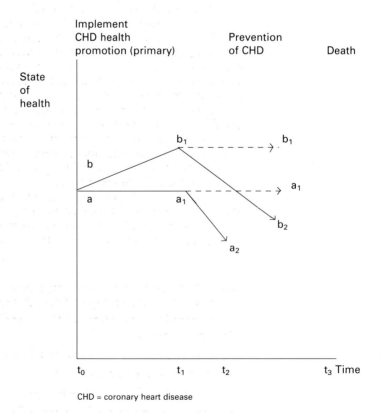

CHD = coronary heart disease

Figure 3. Hypothetical health profiles for an individual.

being places a greater emphasis on improving health status over a lifetime relative to what might otherwise have been expected. In contrast, treatment and curative options can only attempt to minimize a reduction in overall health status for each individual. Figure 3, based on a diagram constructed by Cohen and Henderson (1988) incorporates the prevention and well-being objectives into illustrative time profiles for the health status of an individual.

Assume that at time t_0 a health promotion intervention is implemented that prevents the onset of coronary heart disease for this individual at time t_2. The flat section (a_1) from time t_0 to t_1 represents a relatively healthy individual with no signs of major illness. If at time t_2 ill health from heart disease is prevented then the individual may be expected to maintain his or her health status at the steady state of (a_1) for time t_2 to t_3 (death) or, more likely, there may be some gradual reduction in health status at some point due to other causes of ill health associated with the ageing process (this is represented by the line a_2).

In contrast, assume that the intervention implemented at time t_0 produces benefits in terms of an increase in quality of life (related to health) in the time period t_0 to t_1, in addition to the prevention of heart disease at t_2. This is represented by line (b). Health status may reach a peak at t_1 and then decline (b_2), or remain stable at b_1, but in each case would be expected to be greater than if the 'prevention only' time profile (a_1 or a_2) is followed.

For an economic evaluation, objectives have to be defined in a specific way. An economic objective can be couched in terms of producing lowest costs per unit of outcome or greatest outcomes per unit of cost. As an example, several economic objectives for an excess alcohol consumption screening and health education programme are presented in Table 1. Objective 1 (lowest cost per screening) and 2 (lowest cost per true positive case detected) of Table 1 represent possible objectives for assessing the cost-effectiveness of the alcohol screening programme *per se*. The other objectives relate to the broader aims of health promotion, that is, the prevention of ill health (e.g. life years saved in objective 3) and the promotion of well-being (e.g. quality of life gains in objective 4).

The objectives in Table 1 represent efficiency objectives, that is, identifying the greatest total outcome for the least cost. Depending on the perspective adopted, the analyst may also have equity objectives, that is, gaining the greatest benefit at least cost for a specific group of

Table 1. Possible economic objectives for an excess alcohol consumption screening and health education programme.

1 Lowest cost per screening

2 Lowest cost per true positive alcohol problem case

3 Lowest cost per life year saved

4 Lowest cost per unit gain in quality of life

individuals in society. Therefore, the economic objectives have to have sufficient flexibility to enable higher cost options to be chosen in order to meet equity-orientated targets (see section 8.6). For example, an objective might be the achievement of the lowest cost per unit gain in quality of life for unemployed individuals with an alcohol related problem.

4 Defining the options to include in an economic evaluation of health promotion

4.1 Developing option choices

The range of alternative options to be included in an evaluation of cost-effectiveness has to be carefully assessed, as the validity of the results depends on the most appropriate comparisons being made. For example, a lunchtime workplace aerobics session may prove to be more cost-effective than a series of booklets promoting the health benefits of physical activity. However, if a third appropriate option, which is also potentially more cost effective – such as workplace fitness checks – is not considered, the results could be either misleading or meaningless.

In this review, the rationale that has been adopted for the choice or options to include in an evaluation is that health promotion is an umbrella-type concept, covering a battery of overlapping and interlinking health education, health protection and prevention measures (Tannahill, 1985). In general terms these measures can be distinguished from, for example, preventive drug therapy or surgery in that they do not attempt to provide a specific medical treatment for a diagnostic condition. Instead, health promotion measures involve a range of processes aimed, for example, at protecting people against disease (immunization), inducing health behaviour modification (e.g. smoking cessation), informing and modifying social and professional values and attitudes and lobbying for changes in the social and political environment in which people live (e.g. by reducing poverty, increase in tobacco tax, ban on tobacco advertising).

There are several factors affecting the option choice for an economic evaluation:

1. *The extent to which a clear definition of the dimensions and components of health promotion is provided.*
2. *The scope of the study problem.* Figure 4 (an extension of stage C in Figure 1) lists a range of possible options for assessing resource use efficiency at different levels of decision making. For example, a study with a wide scope (e.g. level 3 or 4, see page 8) might attempt to assist government decision making regarding the cost-effective allocation of resources to health promotion, treatment and care and non-health sector uses. The study scope might be a level 1- or 2-type analysis involving comparison of alternative health promotion options, for example, various health education methods to influence non-health sectors to make policy changes, or a comparison of alternative smoking cessation programmes.
3. *The perspective for the evaluation.* For example, single local provider agencies, national funding bodies or society. Depending on the perspective adopted there may be options that are not considered

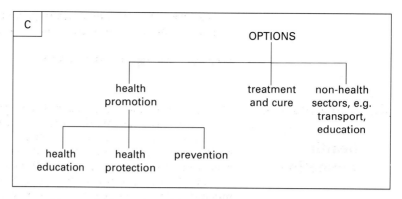

Figure 4. Broad options for economic evaluation.

ethically or politically appropriate. The construction of health promotion quality standards by service providers and other key actors would provide guidance for option choice. For example, these could be used to determine whether a specific health education option targeted at heavy smokers in a socially deprived locality meets predefined ethical standards. The option may be rejected if it appears to be 'victim blaming' (i.e. blaming certain individuals for placing their health at risk from the habits and lifestyle they adopt).

4. *The number of options to be evaluated.* There has to be a minimum of two options to examine relative cost-effectiveness. One of these should be the 'do nothing' option, in which the current method of providing health promotion is compared with alternative strategies which involve some change or new intervention.

There is a need for a classification of the health promotion options that can be used in different levels of cost-effectiveness analysis. The development of this can be addressed in three steps.

1. Examination of developments in thinking regarding the definition and scope of health education, health protection and prevention measures. A standard approach to defining the dimensions of health promotion would assist the production of valid options for cost-effectiveness analysis. If the definitions used are unclear or demonstrate wide variations between studies, then it becomes difficult to compare and interpret the results produced (discussed in section 4.2).

2. The identification of a suitable approach for distinguishing the constituent parts of health promotion. A clearly defined and professionally acceptable model of health promotion is an essential prerequisite of an evaluation of the cost-effectiveness of alternative health promotion options. A model of health promotion developed by Tannahill (1985) appears appropriate as a framework for determining options for cost-effectiveness analysis (discussed in section 4.3).

14

3. The production of a final health promotion option framework suitable for cost-effectiveness analysis (discussed in section 4.4).

Each of these steps is discussed in turn below.

4.2 Defining the dimensions of health promotion

Most of the economic analysis of health promotion has been theoretical and has focused on prevention as an alternative to curative strategies. However, in the few economic evaluations of alternative health promotion interventions conducted to date, little attention has been given to clearly defining the dimensions of the options being appraised. The definition of health promotion represents an area of much debate among health promotion experts which is largely beyond the scope of this report. However, as this is important for option choice in an economic evaluation, a brief review of recent developments in the definition and scope of health education, health protection and disease prevention measures is attempted in this report (for more detailed discussion of this debate see, for example, Tones 1983, 1990; Collins, 1984; Baric, 1985; World Health Organization, 1985). The context of this review is that each measure is viewed as contributing to achieving the objectives of health promotion – the promotion of well-being and the prevention (or at least a reduction in the probability) of disease or ill health.

Health education

Most health educationalists now agree that health education is a key instrument in achieving the objectives of health promotion (Green *et al.*, 1980; Nutbeam, Smith and Catford, 1990). Nutbeam (1986, p. 114) has defined the traditional role of health education as 'concerned mainly with changing the risk behaviour of individuals'. This largely represents the preventive medical approach to health education involving, for example, the provision of medical information on the detrimental health or physiological effects of smoking, high salt intake or taking too little exercise. Among the criticisms levelled at this approach is that it represents a form of 'victim blaming' and ensures health education remains under the control of the medical professionals who might otherwise feel threatened by the prospect of a healthier population with a reduced demand for clinical treatment (Vuori, 1979; Tones, 1983).

Health education can be supplied through various channels and in different settings – these include the use of mass media, teachers, counsellors, doctors, self-help groups providing health education in such settings as the workplace, in hospital, schools, the surgery and other community facilities (Green, 1984). A traditional (and rather outdated) concept of health education that is still adopted by economists is that it is centred around the provision of information, the minimum benefit to the recipients being that they are at least 'informed' (Engleman and Forbes, 1986). Additional benefits may then be derived if health education manages to facilitate attitudinal and behavioural change in individuals towards more healthy lifestyles. In economic terms the potential benefits to society are the increased social and work productivity and possible cost savings (e.g. to the health service) from a healthier population, and for the individual the higher potential life expectancy and quality of life.

Developments in thinking among health promotion experts over the last decade have led to new visions of the role of health education as a central part of the 'new public health' movement (Tones, 1983). The new public health has been defined as the 'professional and public concern with the effect of the total (social, economic and physical) environment in health' (Nutbeam, 1986, p. 122). According to Tones (1990), this has resulted in two new roles for health education:

1. To raise awareness among the public, health education professionals and politicians (and others with power) of the socio-economic and environmental causes of ill health and inequalities in the distribution of health resources. For example, this would cover a political lobbying role for health professionals and public groups to achieve an increase in tobacco taxation set by the government.
2. To generate self-empowerment. This involves the use of health education to provide individuals with the knowledge and lifeskills to enable them to make decisions about their own health and that of their family and the community they live in. For example, this could cover assertiveness training or the provision of education that enables homosexual people to express their sexual rights.

This philosophy of the role of health education has been incorporated into recent health promotion strategy developments. It was an integral part of the health promoting policies designed to reduce social, economic and environmental inequalities outlined by the World Health Organisation in the Ottawa Charter on Health Promotion (Ottawa Charter for Health Promotion, 1986). In addition, in order to raise awareness of socio-economic and health issues and to empower individuals with the skills to change their own circumstances health education has been embodied in the development of the 'healthy cities' initiative (Kickbusch, 1989; Milio, 1990).

The final objective is likely to remain the same whichever concept of the role of health education is adopted and that is to achieve an improved quality of life or well-being for a population. The main difference is the process by which this is achieved. Tones (1983, 1990) argued that health education could be used for political and social awareness raising and for self-empowerment as a central instrument of the process of community development. Such empowerment could be created through the use of existing institutions and procedures if a radical socio-political approach is adopted for health education. This contrasts with the more traditional approach which is orientated towards the individual or involving the development of education and training programmes for health educators, health service personnel and other professionals (e.g. HIV/AIDS awareness training for health and local authority staff).

Health protection

Health protection consists of a set of measures derived from the nineteenth and early twentieth century public health movement (US Department of Health Education and Welfare, 1979). It covers interventions which attempt to influence social, economic and environmental change in a way that is beneficial to health but is normally considered to be outside of the direct control of the individuals it affects (although as a group they can apply pressure for the implementation of health protection measures desired by the majority of community members). Health protection has been defined in general terms as 'legal or fiscal controls, other regulations or policies, and voluntary codes of practice aimed at the enhancement of positive health and the prevention of ill health' (Downie, Fyfe and Tannahill, 1991, p. 51). Such measures would thus include seatbelt legislation, tobacco taxation, pollution control and environmental health, fluoridation of community water supplies, infection control procedures, occupational safety, workplace no-smoking policies and food nutrition labelling.

Health protection measures usually have the prevention of disease or injury as a main objective but have a wider remit in terms of the protection of public health for the benefit of society as a whole. In general, the decision of whether to be 'protected' is not under the control of any one individual, but is delegated to the control of a third party, such as the government or local authority or the company management board. As the implementation of these measures involves changes to the social, economic, environmental and organizational system in which people live, this is likely to be more efficiently undertaken by society's leaders.

A complementary component of health protection is measures designed to provide health support. These include the provision of resources and facilities to enable healthy choices to be made. For example, the promotion of exercise is enhanced by the provision of easily accessible leisure facilities or the availability of aerobic sessions in the workplace. Health education measures could also be used to educate policy makers about the need to supply these facilities and to encourage individuals to make use of them.

Disease prevention

Disease prevention has been defined as 'strategies designed either to reduce risk factors for specific disease, or to enhance host factors that reduce susceptibility to disease' (Nutbeam, 1986). This definition relates to the notion of the primary prevention of disease and injury prior to any signs and symptoms of ill health. A more general definition of primary prevention covers any measures designed to prevent the first occurrence of disease or other phenomenon such as unwanted pregnancy (Tannahill, 1985; Downie, Fyfe and Tannahill 1991). It has also been set in the context of future health status profiles to include 'all efforts to reduce the probability, severity and duration of future illness' (Cohen and Henderson, 1988). The variety of definitions available has led to some confusion over the type of interventions that should be included as primary prevention.

If the Cohen and Henderson (1988) definition is adopted then it covers interventions such as immunization, family planning, pregnancy and infant care, food regulation, tobacco and alcohol taxation, road safety measures, environmental and occupational health and health education targeted at specific risk behaviours. However, it is difficult to reconcile any of these, with the exception of health education, using the definition given by Nutbeam (1986). The confusion arises because Cohen and Henderson include health protection measures within the scope of prevention.

For the purposes of this report and for defining options it is useful to separate health prevention and health protection measures. Primary prevention activities are assumed to consist of strategies such as immunization and family planning (e.g. for unwanted pregnancy) in which the choice of whether to participate is controlled by each individual (there are some exceptions, for example if the prevention measure is mandatory such as the school BCG immunization programme then it is defined as health protection).

There is less uncertainty over the definition of secondary and tertiary prevention measures. The consensus is that the former covers the prevention of avoidable ill health or unwanted outcomes through detection of early signs of disease (through screening for specific diseases or risk factors such as high blood pressure) and subsequent remedial actions or treatment. Tertiary prevention involves the control of more advanced disease to minimize the detrimental impact this has on health (Nutbeam 1986, Cohen and Henderson, 1988).

4.3 Tannahill's model of health promotion

A number of attempts have been made to devise a classification system for health promotion measures, usually linked to the development of public health targets. For example, targets that were set in the government's consultation document for England, *The Health of the Nation* (1991), were classified into treatment, promotion/prevention and rehabilitation groups by Akehurst *et al.* (1991). More specifically the US Department of Health and Human Services identified 22 priority areas for national health promotion and disease prevention, which were grouped into four categories – health promotion, health protection, preventive services and surveillance (Centers for Disease Control, 1990).

Neither of these approaches adequately recognizes the overlaps between the constituent parts of health promotion. Tannahill (1985) has produced a model of health promotion which provides a framework to illustrate the linkages between health education, health protection and prevention. The basic model is represented graphically by three overlapping circles (Figure 5). This produces seven domains which can be used to classify a wide range of health promotion measures and so provides a good basis for classifying option types in an economic evaluation. Figure 5 represents the most recent version of the model which has been slightly modified from the original to allow for a clarification of the interrelationships between positive health (or well-being), empowerment and the prevention of ill health (Downie, Fyfe and Tannahill 1991, p. 58).

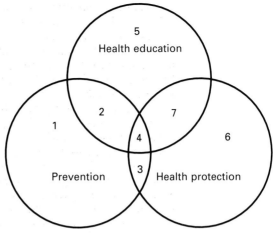

Source: Downie, Fyfe and Tannahill (1991)

Figure 5. Tannahill's model of health promotion.

Each of the domains incorporates both the prevention of ill health and the health promotion objectives of good health and well-being. Domains 5, 6 and 7 cover measures that focus primarily on the well-being objective and domains 1, 2, 3 and 4 focus on measures that have prevention at the forefront. For each domain where health education is included the purpose is either to educate professionals and policy makers or the public (i.e. domains 2, 4, 5 and 7). Each domain and the range of measures included have been described by Downie, Fyfe and Tannahill (1991):

Domain 1: *Prevention.* For example, immunization, screening, self-help groups, nicotine gum for smoking cessation, hypertension case finding.

Domain 2: *Preventive health education.* Education which is aimed at encouraging changes in an individual's health behaviour in order to prevent ill health, and education for service providers to encourage the use of the preventive services. For example, to encourage health professionals to offer alcohol screening or the public to use such facilities.

Domain 3: *Preventive health protection.* For example, water fluoridation, seatbelt legislation, fiscal policy for tobacco/alcohol.

Domain 4: *Protective health education for preventive purposes.* For example, lobbying for seatbelt legislation, for increased tobacco taxation and other efforts to influence the social environment to enhance the probability of effective preventive services being provided.

Domain 5: *Health education for well-being gains* (defined by Downie *et al.* as positive health). This involves education aimed at encouraging changes in an individual's health behaviour in order to promote health gains, such as encouraging a more physically active use of leisure time or changing dietary habits – and empowering individuals/groups to achieve well-being gains (e.g. by increasing their self-esteem).

Domain 6: *Health protection for well-being gains*. For example, the provision of public funds to promote the construction of leisure facilities with the objective of enhancing the well-being of the community, the development of workplace no-smoking policies on the grounds of the general health benefits of clean air.

Domain 7: *Protective health education for well-being gains*. For example, lobbying policy makers for more leisure facilities for the increased well-being of the community, and encouraging and supporting members of the community to express a desire for such facilities.

The use of health education as part of local community development strategies is located across domains 4 and 7. The aim is to use health education to teach life skills and improve knowledge of the social, economic and personal factors that affect health, and to lobby for changes in the social environment through influencing policy.

4.4 Health promotion classification – a schema for option choice

The Tannahill model can be used, with modifications, to generate an option choice framework for the economic evaluation of health promotion. The domains in the model can be used to define categories of similar health promotion options. Three further steps are undertaken here to extend the use of the model for this purpose.

The first step involves the use of the economic concepts of 'supply' and 'demand' to identify the processes involved in each group of health promotion options and so provide a clearer description of the interventions in an appraisal.

'Supply' refers to the process of provision of health promotion and the methods used to optimize the availability of and access to health promoting measures. For example, this would include measures to encourage companies to provide workplace exercise facilities and subsequently the actual provision of these facilities. Educating health professionals to provide health education or screening services would represent a supply side option. A further example is the price and packaging modification of 'healthy' food products by retailers to make these more attractive to consumers, or lobbying to increase tobacco taxation.

'Demand' covers the actual population or risk group coverage and uptake of health promotion interventions. This includes all health education, health protection and prevention services received by individuals, for example, HIV prevention education using mass media, an increase in the tax on tobacco and measures to encourage the use of immunization services.

The second step is to fit the domains of Tannahill's model (1991 version) into these supply–demand process dimensions. The result of this exercise is an extension of Tannahill's model in order to identify more completely the processes involved in the provision of health promotion. This is outlined in Table 2. In order to simplify the use of the model for option choice the domains have been condensed into four groups. Group A represents prevention options (i.e. domain 1). Each of groups B, C and D contain health education and health

Table 2. A framework for health promotion option choice.

Option Groups* (Tannahill model)	Examples of processes	
	Supply dimension	Demand dimension
A – Domain 1 Prevention	Provision of immunization/ screening services, self-help groups, availability of nicotine gum.	Public/target groups exposure to and use of immunization and screening services, self-help groups, nicotine gum.
B – Domains 2 and 5 Health education	Health Education for professionals/other service providers to encourage the provision of immunization screening services or to promote physical activity for quality of life benefits.	Public/target groups exposure to and use of health education to increase awareness and encourage uptake of immunization/screening services, to empower individuals to be able to influence their health behaviour.
C – Domains 3 and 6 Health protection / support	Provision of exercise facilities, company no-smoking policies, passing of seatbelt legislation, water fluoridation agreements, tobacco/ alcohol fiscal policy.	Public/target group exposure to and use of leisure facilities, adherence to no-smoking policy. Public/target groups use of seatbelts, fluoridized water (should be 100% of car drivers and water consumers in areas of fluoridation), cigarette/ alcohol consumption.
D – Domains 4 and 7 Progressive health education (e.g., community development strategies)	Use of health education to encourage policy makers/other influential bodies to provide health protective or health enhancing measures or to influence the social environment in such a way as to create pressures for such change	Use of health education to empower public/target groups to lobby and encourage policy makers/ other influential bodies to provide health protective or health enhancing measures. Empowerment of individuals or communities to improve their social environment in a way conducive to improved well-being or the prevention of ill health.

* Each of groups B, C and D incorporates both prevention of ill health and promotion of well-being dimensions of health promotion.

protection options aimed at the prevention of ill health and/or the promotion of well-being (positive health).

The third step is to define the options for an economic evaluation. For example, one option might be that of training health service staff to provide health education on smoking cessation with the objective of preventing future heart disease (included under the supply dimensions of group B/domain 2 – preventive health education – in Table 2). An alternative option could be the use of mass media health education. This would involve assessment of the public/target group exposure to and uptake of the message, and so include assessment of the demand dimension of group B domain 2 in Table 2. However, a full examination of the processes involved in the use of such health education would also require an understanding of the supply processes involved (e.g. how and why mass media has been used as the medium for health education).

The purpose of Table 2 is not to produce a definitive model of health promotion, but to generate an option choice framework for an economic evaluation and to induce further discussion of the best way to define health promotion options. It also provides an example of how Tannahill's model can be used and demonstrates the need to define carefully the health promotion options for the purposes of evaluating the cost-effectiveness of alternative strategies.

4.5 Constructing health education options

Section 4.4 has outlined a general method for defining the processes involved in different health promotion options. This section provides more detail on defining specific options for groups B and D of Table 2 i.e. health education measures. This is done by assuming the purpose of an economic evaluation is to assess the cost-effectiveness of alternative health education interventions (i.e. a level 1-type analysis, see section 3.2).

In addition to defining supply and demand processes, an initial stage in the construction of a health education option is to define the component parts, which consist of three basic dimensions: the setting/channel for delivery (e.g. workplace/mass media), the risk-factor strategy adopted and the broad objectives of the intervention (i.e. the disease prevention and/or health promotion objectives, such as prevention of coronary heart disease, prevention of lung cancer and promotion of health).

Each of these dimensions have to be considered when defining a health education option. For example, a health education option which has prevention of coronary heart disease as its primary focus would also need to be defined in terms of a choice between a multi-risk factor strategy (e.g. combining diet, exercise and smoking into one health eduction programme) or a single-risk factor strategy (e.g. smoking cessation only) and the choice of one or more settings/channels for the intervention. Alternatively, the starting point for developing an option could be the setting/channel, such as the workplace or the risk factor strategy (single- or multi-risk factor). To determine overall effectiveness, especially for multi-risk factor strategies, it is important to also assess the total prevention impact (for all related diseases) of the intervention.

Health promotion setting/channel	Multi-risk factor	Single-risk factor
Workplace	diet, smoking, exericise	stress management
School	general health education	healthy diet education
Community	CHD programme	alcohol risk education
Mass media	HIV infection and campaign	no-smoking campaign
Primary care	health checks and advice	counselling for smoking cessation
	Complete programme	Complete programme

* Note: a third dimension is the disease/health orientation of the option and a fourth dimension would cover the use of health education for self empowerment (in different settings).

CHD = coronary heart disease

Figure 6. Two-dimension option framework for health education* – some examples of options.

Figure 6 outlines an option framework for health education with some illustrative examples. This contains two dimensions: (1) the alternative settings/channels for health education and (2) single versus multi-risk factor strategies. A third dimension – the disease orientation – depends on the links between risk factors and disease (e.g. diet, cholesterol and coronary heart disease). For example, at one level the options to be compared could be advice from a GP to stop smoking versus a workplace health education scheme comprising information on the benefits of exercise, diet advice and other health education. Alternatively, multi- or single-risk factor strategies can be compared across settings/channels, for example, workplace versus school versus mass media. Combining the two dimensions would result in a comparison of multi-setting single-risk factor interventions (e.g. no-smoking day events) and multi-setting multi-risk factor interventions (for example, Heartbeat Wales or Look After Your Heart in England). A further dimension would be to use the settings/ channels in Figure 6 as the basis for describing community development strategies using health education as an instrument for the increased empowerment of individuals. Most evaluations of the effectiveness and cost-effectiveness of health education in the literature have not considered this approach to health education.

The discussion above has focused on the 'demand' elements of health education options. The 'supply' aspects of each option also have to be considered. In addition, it may be appropriate to incorporate (or at least control for) the contribution of health protection and health support measures such as food nutrition labelling, tobacco fiscal policy and the provision of workplace exercise facilities.

An important consideration is whether to target health education at a specific group of people. For instance, the workplace may be considered by health promotion managers as an appropriate setting for a single-risk factor health education strategy focusing on the reduction in alcohol consumption, which has the objective of improving the current well-being of workers who drink to excess.

The choice of the workplace setting identifies the broad target group as the employees of the companies involved. However, the target group may be more specifically defined as a sub-section of employees, either those identified as having alcohol related problems or with other characteristics thought to be relevant (e.g. aged between 40–50 years, males only).

This leads into the issue of the choice between a 'high risk group' strategy and a 'population' strategy for health education. The high risk group strategy involves targeting the health education intervention at those identified as at-risk of ill health. In the workplace, for example, this would involve screening employees for evidence of excessive alcohol consumption and providing health education only to those 'at-risk' individuals. Hence, with this approach the focus is on the individual and his or her health behaviour. In contrast, a population strategy attempts to change the prevalence of the risk factor (alcohol consumption) in the whole group (World Health Organization, 1990). Education is therefore directed at all employees regardless of their alcohol consumption habits.

A relevant study problem for economic evaluation would be to compare the cost-effectiveness of high risk and population options. For example, Berwick, Cretin and Keeler (1981) compared the cost per life year saved from a high risk strategy – screening for high cholesterol levels in a cohort of 10-year-old-boys plus the provision of individual dietary advice for those identified as at-risk, with a population mass media/school based campaign for the complete cohort, producing evidence in favour of the latter (see section 9.3).

5 Study design choices for evaluating efficacy and effectiveness

5.1 Efficacy, effectiveness and efficiency

Before starting on an economic evaluation which focuses on efficiency it is necessary to establish the efficacy of the options that are to be considered. Efficacy refers to establishing, under controlled study conditions, that an intervention results in an improved outcome (Engleman and Forbes, 1986). If this is not proven then the assessment of efficiency is of no relevance (Drummond, Stoddart and Torrance, 1987b). The effectiveness of an intervention is established by examining whether it improves outcomes (such as health status) in actual settings. The data generated by an effectiveness evaluation is likely to be of most direct use for a cost-effectiveness evaluation.

The purpose of establishing efficacy and effectiveness can be demonstrated by using health education as an example. When establishing the efficiency of dietary health education compared to a 'do-nothing' option for reducing mortality and morbidity from coronary heart disease, it is necessary to have evidence of the efficacy of dietary modification programmes. Efficacy may be established if the weight of epidemiological evidence suggests that under optimal study conditions a reduction in fat consumption by an individual reduces cholesterol levels and leads to reduced mortality or morbidity from heart disease. Effectiveness, however, will only be established if the dietary health education intervention is tested in actual settings, for example as part of a community heart disease programme (such as the Heartbeat Wales Demonstration Programme). The intervention is then subject to a range of confounding factors which may result in effectiveness not being proven, even if efficacy has been established. Both need to be established for an efficiency evaluation to be of relevance.

5.2 Types of study design

An important consideration is that the evaluation of cost-effectiveness represents only a partial analysis (Drummond, Stoddart and Torrance 1987b). In a full evaluation the construction of a rigorous and reliable study design is very important to enable the assignment of specific outcomes to different interventions. There are three broad types of study design that have been used in the evaluation of this relationship for health promotion and prevention interventions: experimental, quasi-experimental and non-experimental (Figure 7 – an extension of stage D in Figure 1).

A wide literature is available on the purpose and merits of each type of evaluation (for a review see Donaldson and Russell 1991). A brief description of the use of each design for health promotion evaluations is provided here:

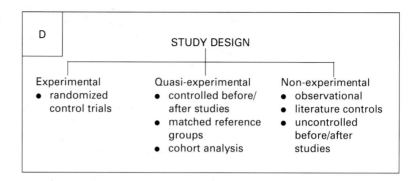

Figure 7. Alternative types of study design.

1. *Experimental designs.* Such designs are used to establish the efficacy of health promotion interventions. This usually takes the form of a randomized control trial whereby programme participants are randomly assigned to one or more trial intervention groups and control groups. The design is very structured and if properly constructed will enable rigorous statistical analysis to be conducted.

2. *Quasi-experimental designs.* When it is not practical to construct a randomized control trial, as is often the case for health promotion interventions, then recourse can be made to the use of quasi-experimental designs, for example 'before and after' studies containing a control group, or matching an intervention population with a control population on a number of common characteristics (Leiderkerken *et al.*, 1990). Such designs are most often used for the evaluation of the effectiveness of interventions in actual settings rather than under controlled study conditions (Engleman and Forbes, 1986).

3. *Non-experimental designs.* Studies incorporating such designs represent the least rigorous and reliable approach to establishing the effectiveness of health promotion, mainly because of the exclusion of a control group or the availability of actual data. A higher reliance is placed on the use of assumptions drawn from the literature or from prior epidemiological evidence (Donaldson and Russell, 1991).

The criteria for the use of each type of study design for health promotion evaluation has been fully explained by Green (1979), but in general health promotion studies adopting non-experimental designs provide insufficient rigour for economic analysis (Leiderkerken *et al.*, 1990).

It has been argued that the assessment of the efficacy and effectiveness of health promotion interventions should be incorporated within a single systematic research design (Flay 1986). A developmental model for the comprehensive evaluation of health education has been devised by Nutbeam, Smith and Catford (1990). This model is generated by a theoretical framework consisting of inputs from epidemiology, behavioural and social sciences and intervention theory. Three evaluation questions are then posed in the model: (1) Does the intervention work? (i.e. an assessment of efficacy). The emphasis here is on outcome evaluation using an experimental study design. (2) Can the intervention be repeated and refined? This involves a mixture of process and outcome evaluation using a quasi-experimental study design, for example, heart disease demonstration studies such as Heartbeat Wales. (3) Can the intervention be widely implemented. This generally involves the use of practical (non-experimental) dissemination studies to examine the process of implementing health education programmes. The second and third questions focus on the measurement of the effectiveness of the intervention in actual settings.

Nutbeam, Smith and Catford (1990) identified a further stage – that of operational management. This covers the measurement and the costs and benefits of health education programmes and the identification of performance indicators. However, it may be helpful not to separate this element of evaluation from the main body of health promotion evaluation. In order to minimize the cost of conducting a complete evaluation a more appropriate strategy would be to incorporate an economic evaluation *within* the analysis of programme effectiveness. Such integration was attempted with the North Karelia Heart disease programme in Finland (Bjorkquist *et al*, 1979). However, this example provides the exception rather than the rule for demonstration studies.

5.3 Internal and external validity

The choice of study design for the evaluation of health promotion effectiveness emphasizes the problems of the trade-off between internal validity and external validity (Liederkerken *et al.*, 1990). Internal validity refers to the extent to which a study design can be used to attribute changes in outcome to the inputs of the intervention – the analysis of efficacy. External validity is the assessment of whether the effects of an intervention established under controlled conditions are generalizable to the wider population, that is the analysis of effectiveness in actual settings. The problem for health promotion evaluation is in achieving an even balance between internal and external validity.

In most instances internal validity can be achieved by the use of experimental designs, in particular a randomized control trial (Cochrane, 1972), in which confounding variables can be controlled. Whilst this may be a feasible approach for evaluating the efficacy of a new drug treatment, for many health promotion interventions, especially community based programmes, the use of such a study design is implausible (Altman, 1986; Nutbeam, Smith and Catford 1990,).

Even if an experimental study design is used, internal validity can be threatened in two main ways – firstly, if no effects are established even though they are present and secondly, if the effects are established but are incorrectly attributed to the intervention (Liederkerken *et al.*, 1990). However, any deviation from the pursuit of rigid internal validity will also increase the probability of bias in the effectiveness results, in particular the problems of selection and confounding factor bias (Donaldson and Russell 1991). Selection bias occurs if the intervention and control group have different socio-economic or demographic characteristics that affect outcomes. Confounding factor bias occurs when the effects are thought to be linked to the health promotion intervention but are instead caused by exogenous factors. This bias is more likely to occur in a quasi-experimental study such as Heartbeat Wales or in a non-experimental study than it is in a randomized control trial.

Internal validity is an essential precursor to determining external validity but the methodological difficulties of setting up an experimental study design to establish the former are so great for many types of health promotion intervention that most studies have focused on the latter and assumed (either explicitly or implicitly) internal validity (Green, 1979). In general only single-risk factor (e.g. smoking cessation or diet modification) or single-setting interventions (e.g. workplace or school) have been suitable for the use of experimental designs (Duncan, Stein and Cummings, 1991; Simons-Morten et al., 1991). Such studies have tended to involve the selection of high risk individuals such as smokers or those screened as having a high blood cholesterol levels. The multiple risk factor intervention trial (MRFIT) smoking cessation programme in the US used a randomized control trial study design to assign over 600 smokers to an intervention group who received smoking cessation education and support and a control group who received usual care for smoking related illness. The study concluded that the clinical trial results supported the inference from observational studies that smoking cessation education can have an important effect on permanent quit rates (33% in the trial group against 20% in the control) and reducing pulmonary function in heavy smokers (Browner et al., 1990).

The use of a randomized control trial for evaluating the effectiveness of health promotion on behavioural change is fraught with difficulties because of the need for informed consent and the behavioural bias caused by the use of structured and unnatural study conditions (Green, 1979). Behavioural change is far more reliably predicted if it is determined in actual settings. In the context of health promotion interventions the benefits of achieving external validity may well outweigh the cost in terms of a reduction in internal validity (Green, 1979; Pocock and Thompson, 1990).

Because of the difficulties of using randomized controlled trials to establish causal relationships most large scale community based interventions, such as mass media education and coronary heart disease demonstration studies, have assessed effectiveness by adopting quasi-experimental study designs. Examples of community based heart disease studies are the Stanford Five Cities programme (Farquhar et al., 1990) and the Heartbeat Wales project (Nutbeam and Catford, 1987) which use a range of types of health education and behavioural intervention across several settings in the community. This makes it very difficult to randomly allocate individuals in the study population to intervention and control groups. Instead the Heartbeat Wales programme conducted a community survey with over 21,000 households covering nine regions of Wales representing the intervention group and matched these with a reference group from a neighbouring region in England. Similarly in the Stanford Five Cities programme three cities were ascribed for health education and the impact on risk factor levels and coronary heart disease mortality compared with two reference cities.

6 Measuring the costs of health promotion

6.1 Overview

Cost is specifically defined in an economic evaluation – the cost of resources used in one health programme is the value foregone from their use in an alternative programme (known in economic terms as the opportunity cost). For example, the time a doctor spends giving a patient advice about the health risks of smoking can not be re-used to treat another patient for hypertension. Hence the cost of a smoking advice programme in the doctor's surgery would include the value of the doctor's time diverted from other activities. A zero cost would only exist if the doctor has sufficient work-time flexibility to provide smoking advice without giving up any of the time spent with other patients or on other activities and without working longer hours, as leisure time also has a value.

6.2 The measurement of costs

There are three interrelated issues to consider in evaluating the costs of a health promotion programme:

1. The type of costs included.
2. The collection of data for cost estimation.
3. The production of a cost estimate.

These are summarized in Figure 8, which represents an extension of stage E in the economic evaluation framework (see Figure 1, chapter 2).

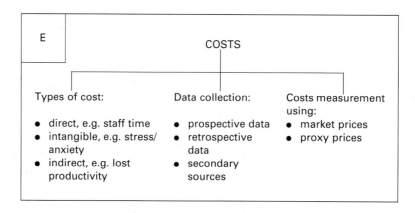

Figure 8. Issues in cost measurement.

Types of cost

There is more than one type of cost that needs to be considered in an economic evaluation of health promotion activities. Which costs are included depends on the perspective of the study (see section 3.2). A full evaluation of the costs of health promotion from a societal perspective would include all costs incurred by a range of agencies and by individuals receiving health promotion. Direct costs cover the staff, materials, capital and other resources invested in a health promotion programme by the agencies involved in its provision (e.g. HEA, health authorities and local authorities) and the time and out-of-pocket money expenses incurred by individuals participating in the programme. For example, a range of costs are likely to be incurred through the use of a Health Promotion Officer (HPO), employed by the District Health Authority, to provide public exercise promotion sessions in a local community centre. The direct costs to the providing agencies include the time of the HPO, the expenses incurred by that staff member (e.g. travel) and any additional costs from using the community centre facilities for the purpose of providing health education rather than for some other socially beneficial use.

The costs to the individual participants are the time and money expenses of travelling to the community centre and attending the exercise education session. This only represents a cost to the individual if they would not have otherwise incurred this expense in their normal daily activities. This explains why health promotion activities are often located in settings which people visit for other purposes such as GP surgeries and the workplace. For example, by providing health education as part of the routine visit to the GP for a health check, the time and money incurred by the individual can be minimized without incurring additional costs to the providing agency, in this case the health service.

Other psycho-social problems such as the stress and anxiety incurred in participating in a health promotion programme are known in economic terms as intangible costs. Arguments against breast cancer screening have as a central tenet the perception of high intangible costs from anxiety caused by the invitation to attend and from the low specificity of the screening device causing a high probability of a false positive result, that is, if individuals are tested incorrectly as having the disease (Holland and Steward, 1991). As a second example of intangible costs, a national HIV prevention mass media campaign carried out in the UK was criticized as being ineffective because of the widespread fear and alienation from the central message that it created among the sexually active population (Wellings and McVey, 1990).

An indirect cost is the loss of the 'production value' to society of an individual's time spent participating in a health programme. For example, a company may provide breast cancer screening for a selection of its female employees during work time. This would represent a cost to the company (and society) in terms of the 'lost work time' of the women attending screening. However, women attending a breast screening clinic who are not employed may also generate indirect costs through the diversion of their time from activities which (usually) have a positive value to society but do not receive a payment (e.g. this could be voluntary work or housework). Indirect costs should only be included in an evaluation if the cost derives from participation in a health promotion programme and not if the 'productivity losses' would have occurred anyway due to the individual's health condition (Drummond, Stoddart and Torrance 1987b). For example, an individual may not be able to carry out his or her normal work activities because of illness related to alcohol consumption and not because of their attendance at a clinic to control his or her drinking habits.

The summation of direct, intangible and indirect costs to society of health promotion programmes represents the total *gross cost* of the intervention. For evaluations that adopt a narrow perspective of the single agency provider (e.g. a regional health authority) only the direct costs to that agency will be included. Few studies are likely to include all cost categories, especially intangible and indirect costs which are difficult to measure accurately and reliably.

An alternative approach is to calculate the total *net costs* of each health promotion option. This approach includes each of the components covered above, but subtracts any resource savings that can be identified to the health service, individual participants and other agencies.

Resource savings from a health promotion programme implemented in the current time period may be achieved in the future from a reduction in ill health and hence lower use of health service facilities. However, recent research has suggested that health promotion and prevention does not produce resource savings because of an increased demand for health care and other support (e.g. pensions) from an ageing population (Warner, 1987). Whatever the outcome, a net cost approach can be used to incorporate potential costs and savings.

Data collection and cost estimation

The second issue in measuring costs is the choice of method of data collection on resource use for each health promotion option considered. Prospective data collection using monitoring forms and time diaries enables resource use to be identified as it is incurred. However, this would require a close monitoring of costs incurred by each of the provider agencies and by individual recipients (if a societal perspective is adopted). This could be time consuming and expensive – for example a detailed diary would need to be kept by individuals to record their participation in a health promotion activity.

Alternatively, data could be collected retrospectively, for example from the use of questionnaires to service providers on resources used and to individual recipients to recall their time and money expenses, and through examination of accounts and previous cost estimates.

A third approach would be to derive estimates of resource use based on the judgement of professionals involved in providing the health promotion programme. Similarly, secondary data from similar programmes that may have been undertaken could be used. It is particularly difficult to accurately estimate the specific use for a health promotion activity of resources such as premises, heating, lighting and administration which in many cases are shared between several diverse uses (for example, health education may be carried out in a GP surgery along with all other primary care activities). This approach provides the least reliable estimates of resource use. A range of estimates would need to be presented to allow for imprecision in the 'best' cost estimate.

Even if reliable data on resource use can be collected, there remains the problem of deriving an accurate valuation of resource inputs in order to derive cost estimates. The salary rate paid, for example, to a health professional providing dietary advice, represents the value in the health care labour market of such specialist staff. In general 'market' values (or prices) for staff, equipment and supplies provide the most readily available and convenient measure to estimate costs.

The most basic approach to costing is to use information on financial expenditures available on the annual accounts of providers of health promotion services. However, often resources used in a health promotion programme do not appear as an additional cost on the accounts of a provider agency. The use of existing nurses in a hospital to undertake screening of patient admissions for excess alcohol consumption may not be recorded as a cost for that specific programme. The nurses may be seen as 'free' because they are already employed at the hospital. Nevertheless, there is a cost because their time has been diverted from providing other nursing care in order to undertake the screening.

In addition, a resource used in a health promotion programme may appear to have no financial cost or 'market price', but has an alternative use value. In this case, a proxy measure has to be used as an estimate of the value of the resource. For example, the time costs of an individual attending a self-help smoking cessation group could be valued using an estimate of the value of work time (i.e. earnings) or leisure time that has been given up. (Research has shown that individuals value leisure time, on average, at 25% of work earnings.)

Similarly, for resources which have a market price this may only reflect the financial cost to the purchasing agency and not the actual value to society. For example, a health authority may purchase screening devices at 'excessive prices' because of a reliance on one provider. This price would be appropriate to use when estimating the financial cost of screening to the health authority, but not the cost to society of implementing a screening programme. Once again, proxy prices would be required.

Finally, some costs are impossible to estimate reliably – for example, no good method as yet exists for assessing the costs of anxiety and stress to an individual which may be caused by such things as a misleading health education campaign (e.g. excess worry from mass media HIV prevention campaigns among people at low risk of infection).

7 Measuring the outcomes of health promotion

7.1 Overview

To compare the cost-effectiveness of alternative options, an appropriate outcome measure is required. For example, it would not be possible to directly compare the cost-effectiveness of a smoking cessation health education option with an alcohol education option if programme-specific measures such as reductions in smoking prevalence or changes in alcohol consumption were used. In this case, a more general outcome measure would be required, such as potential life years saved from each programme.

There are three interrelated types of outcome measure that can be used: process indicators, intermediate outcomes and final outcomes (see Figure 9, which represents an extension of stage F in Figure 1, chapter 2). Which one is used will depend on the scope of the evaluation and perspective adopted (see section 3.2), the data availability and the type of health promotion option(s) included in the evaluation (see section 4.4 and Table 2, chapter 4). Process indicators can be divided into two sets: those measuring the effectiveness of the supply of a health promotion option (i.e. the process of delivery) and those measuring effectiveness in terms of the demand for a health promotion option (i.e. the public/target group coverage, awareness and uptake).

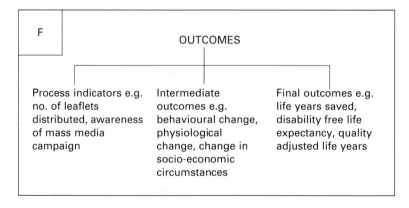

Figure 9. Outcome measures for health promotion options.

7.2 Types and use of outcome measure

A set of process indicators (incorporating supply and demand dimensions) and intermediate and final outcome measures can be determined for each of the four health promotion option groups described in section 4.4 (see Table 2, chapter 4). Examples of outcome measures are presented in Table 3. Option group A consists of prevention measures. A distinct set of process measures can be used to measure the output of these activities. The process indicators and intermediate outcome measures for each of the other option groups reflect the two dimensions of the Tannahill model of the prevention of ill health and the promotion of well-being (positive health).

Broad comparisons of options across the four groups can be made by using a common final outcome measure. However, the effectiveness of health promotion programmes in terms of the provision, coverage, uptake and behavioural or social/environmental change associated with (and prior to) any changes in health status are measured by process indicators and intermediate outcome measures.

Each type of outcome measure is discussed below.

Table 3. Examples of process indicators and outcome measures.

| Option group† | Process indicators | | Outcome measures* | |
	supply	demand	intermediate	final
A Domain 1 Prevention	Number of clinics providing screening or immunization services.	Number receiving screening or immunization among target group.	N/A	Change in health status.
B Domains 2 and 5 Health education	Number of clinics aware of benefits of providing screening or immunization services.	Number aware of or receiving screening or immunization among target group.	N/A	Change in health status.
	Number of health professionals providing dietary health education.	Public uptake of dietary health education.	Reduction in mean dietary fat consumption/ cholesterol levels.	Change in health status.
C Domains 3 and 6 Health protection/ support	Indicator of extent of seatbelt legislation/level of increase in tobacco taxation.	Indicator of attitudes among public to tobacco fiscal policy/ seatbelt legislation.	Reduction in smoking prevalence/use of seatbelts.	Change in health status.

Table 3. Continued

	Number of leisure facilities built/ number of companies with no-smoking policies.	Number using new leisure facilities/ adhering to no-smoking policy.	Increase in fitness levels/reduction in smoking prevalence in workplace.	Change in health status.
D Domains 4 and 7 Progressive health education/ community development	Indicator of provision of health education to empower groups/ communities to lobby for health related improvements in the social environment and health protection policy.	Indicator of extent to which pressure groups/ communities lobby for health related improvements in their social environment and health protection policy (e.g. increases in tobacco taxation).	Reduction in smoking prevalence (e.g. due to an increase in tobacco taxation following lobbying pressure).	Change in health status.
	Indicator of change in socio-economic environment (e.g. reduced poverty, increase in damp-proofed houses, greater access to leisure facilities).	Awareness of increase in health enhancing possibilities among public/target group.	Increase in informed health behaviour choices or perceived well-being (e.g. resulting in a reduction in smoking prevalence/lower mean dietary fat consumption).	Change in health status.

* The outcomes in this table are intended to be illustrative. Actual evidence of a causal association between process indicators, intermediate outcomes and final outcomes requires the control of other confounding factors which might influence the outcomes.
† See Table 2 in chapter 4.
N/A Not appropriate.

Process indicators

Process indicators are measures of the delivery and dissemination of health promotion and health education interventions (Altman, 1986; Nutbeam, Smith and Catford 1990). The objective of an evaluation at this level is to examine how a health promotion intervention such as a mass media healthy eating campaign might be expected to operate. For example, this might involve a subjective assessment of the acceptability of a health education message to health professionals, community leaders and individual recipients, and examination of the processes by which a coronary heart disease health education campaign can achieve maximum assimilation into the infrastructure of the community at greatest risk of heart disease.

A qualitative examination of the dynamic processes involved in the delivery of health promotion is an important part of any evaluation in order to help understand how a programme might work in practice.

However, in an economic evaluation, quantitative process indicators are required to provide a measure of service delivery effectiveness. They represent programme-specific measures and so cannot be used to directly compare the effectiveness of different types of health promotion programmes. In terms of Table 3, such process indicators can only be used for intra-option group comparisons and not for comparing options from different groups.

In Table 3, examples of process indicators are presented for each option group with a distinction made between the supply and demand dimensions of these indicators. For health education options (group B) the effectiveness of educating health professionals such as GPs to provide dietary advice to their patients could be measured by a 'supply' process indicator such as the proportion of GPs providing health education on diet. The impact of this approach to providing dietary health education could then be measured by a 'demand' process indicator such as the number of patients actually receiving and understanding the dietary advice provided by the GP. Alternatively, a process indicator for the impact of a HIV mass media campaign could be the public awareness of the initiative and the messages it conveys. Similarly, a range of supply and demand process indicators could be used for options covered by other option groups, as is illustrated in Table 3.

In a cost-effectiveness analysis, process indicators might be used to compare alternative strategies for delivering dietary health education. For example, the use of a mass media campaign promoting the consumption of low fat, high fibre food products could be compared with a leaflet promotion carrying the same messages, using the level of public awareness of each strategy as the measure of relative process effectiveness.

Intermediate outcomes

These represent the influence of health promotion on the behaviour of an individual. This link could be direct, for example, if a no-smoking day results in 0.5% of smokers quitting permanently, or indirect, for example, health education initially may be aimed at empowering individuals to make informed health choices and hence ultimately result in a reduction in smoking prevalence in a community. Behaviour change represents the middle stage between the provision and uptake of health promotion (i.e. process) and impact on final health outcomes. To have any impact, health promotion first needs to be provided to and acted upon by those individuals or groups it is meant to reach. Subsequently, the measurement of the direct or indirect impact on individual choice and health behaviour depends on the type of intervention being considered (i.e. according to the option group it corresponds with). Table 3 provides examples of intermediate outcome measures for each option group. The appropriate type of intermediate outcome measure varies according to the range of options included in the evaluation:

1. For health education options aimed at promoting well-being

(option group B) and for some health protection or support options such as the provision of leisure facilities (option group C) the appropriate intermediate outcome measure is represented by a voluntary change in individual health behaviour and/or an associated change in physiological risk factors. For example, the effectiveness of dietary health education among the public can be measured by assessing changes in food purchasing patterns (e.g. to identify a shift to lower fat foods among an intervention group) or by measuring the cholesterol levels over time of a sample of public exposed to health education compared to those not receiving advice. The effectiveness of a health support measure such as an increase in leisure facilities in a locality may be measured by examining relative changes in the fitness levels of users/local residents.

2. The majority of health protection options (group C) influence health behaviour through formal group agreement, policy, regulation or coercion rather than individual choice. For example, mandatory or voluntary no-smoking policies in the workplace, seatbelt legislation and water fluoridation policies constrain the choices of, respectively, smokers, car drivers and tap water consumers. The effect of these health protective interventions could be measured using intermediate outcomes, for example, by assessing changes in total tobacco consumption among employees, the actual use of seatbelts and changes in levels of tap water consumption (e.g. a reduced consumption of tap water, substituted by bottled water, demonstrates a detrimental outcome for a water fluoridation policy). An increase in tobacco tax, in principle, allows the individual to choose whether or not to change his or her smoking behaviour, and effectiveness can be measured by monitoring changes in tobacco consumption. In practice, the use of such fiscal policy is likely to operate as a financial constraint on individuals' choice regarding their health behaviour and lifestyle.

3. Prevention activities, such as immunization, screening and preventive self-help groups (option group A and domain 2 in group B) do not have an obvious intermediate outcome for measuring effectiveness. For example, screening for alcohol related problems or for high cholesterol levels is not likely by itself to change health behaviour or the social circumstances affecting health behaviour. If prevention interventions such as screening are followed up by the provision of health education, then an intermediate outcome measure can be used to assess the effectiveness of the whole programme, e.g. the reduction in excess alcohol consumption among high-risk drinkers, due to a combined alcohol screening and health education programme.

Immunization does not require a change in health behaviour to be effective at preventing specific disease. The behavioural link between immunization and the prevention of ill health concerns the decision of individuals be immunized (e.g. for measles), which is included as a demand process indicator.

4. For progressive health education and local community development strategies (option group D) two types of intermediate

outcome measure appear to be appropriate.

Firstly, a range of behavioural change indicators can be used (e.g. changes in smoking prevalence, increase in exercise, reduction in stress, improvement in diet) to assess the ultimate effectiveness of empowering health education interventions aimed at inducing (e.g. through lobbying pressure) changes in the social environment or in health protection policy (e.g. tobacco taxation, seatbelt legislation). It may not be feasible or appropriate to monitor health behaviour change because of the complexities of deriving an association between such change and health education strategies (or community development programmes).

A second approach is to attempt to adopt a measure of change in 'informed health choice opportunities'. For example, where people are living in socially deprived areas with low incomes, health education and community development strategies may be used to reduce feelings of lack of control over health choices. This may also be combined with efforts from local community pressure groups to lobby local government to tackle, for example, the problem of damp housing. Appropriate indicators could be devised to measure, firstly, increases in number of houses damp-proofed and secondly, the perceived benefits (in terms of an improved feeling of well-being, or control over personal health) of individuals affected by this change. Again, the link with measurable changes in health behaviour (e.g. smoking, diet) is tenuous and not necessarily appropriate. This represents an intriguing area for future research in terms of devising appropriate measures of outcome.

The actual measurement of intermediate outcomes, in particular health behaviour modification, is not a simple task. A problem exists in assessing attributability – the extent to which the health promotion intervention (e.g. health education for diet or smoking change) is the cause of any changes in health behaviour (Altman, 1986; Liederkerken et al., 1990). It is likely that behaviour change will be related to a wide range of other factors, such as community attitudes to diet/smoking or the availability of transport to get to out-of-town supermarkets selling 'healthy foods'.

As was discussed in section 5.3, a randomized trial could be adopted to control for such confounding factors. However, this approach is usually limited to small scale interventions and raises the whole question of whether it is appropriate to exclude the effect on individuals' health behaviour or responses to health education of their actual social and economic circumstances. Instead a quasi-experimental study design, in which behaviour change is assessed in actual settings and can be affected by a wide range of factors, might be used at the cost of some loss of outcome attributable to the specific health promotion intervention.

In addition, there usually exists uncertainty in the epidemiological association between behavioural change and change in physiological risk factors, such as between diet and cholesterol levels. Because of this uncertainty it may not be possible to attribute a reduction in cholesterol levels to a modification in diet among a group who receive dietary health education.

By measuring intermediate outcomes, a distinction can be made between the direct and total impact of a health promotion intervention on health behaviour; for example, the direct impact of workplace health education relates to behavioural change among employees exposed to the education. The total impact would include the secondary impact of health education, whereby modifications in employees' behaviour also influences the behaviour of their family and others in the community with which they interact.

A further issue relevant for measuring intermediate outcomes is to examine the processes involved – *how* improved outcomes are achieved is an important element of determining and interpreting *what* improved outcomes are actually achieved. This is not simple to understand but reiterates the need to examine both qualitative and quantitative supply and demand processes (as suggested in the previous section) in addition to intermediate outcomes for each health promotion option in the evaluation.

The use of intermediate outcomes to compare the relative effectiveness of different health promotion options is limited. For example, it would not be possible to directly compare a dietary health education intervention that achieves a reduction in cholesterol levels with a smoking cessation programme that achieves a reduction in smoking prevalence. However, there is some scope for using intermediate outcomes to compare across option groups, for example, smoking cessation health education (group B) and increases in tobacco tax (group C) could be compared using changes in tobacco consumption as the outcome measure.

Intermediate outcomes provide data that can be used as a basis for the estimation of final health outcomes, such as mortality and morbidity reduction, and quality of life gains.

Final health outcomes

The general objectives of health promotion have been defined as the prevention of disease and ill health and the promotion of good health or well-being. In order to evaluate the cost-effectiveness of alternative health promotion options in meeting these objectives a final outcome measure which assesses changes in health status is required. A number of alternative final outcome measures exist which can be grouped according to the extent to which they provide a proxy measure of overall health status.

Firstly, economists have favoured the development of health status measures which attempt to combine several elements of individual well-being into a single numerical scale incorporating physical, mental and social activity dimensions. These have the advantage of encompassing a wide range of general health status attributes and so provide the best approach for comparing the health impact of different health promotion, disease prevention and curative interventions. Within an economic evaluation such scales provide a comprehensive measure of health outcomes that can be combined with cost data to determine priorities for allocating resources between health programmes (Drummond, 1989).

There are several such numerical scales that have been developed for health programme outcome measurement (see Kind, 1988). Two examples of health status scales used in actual evaluations are the British Rosser matrix used to derive quality adjusted life years (QALYs) (Kind, Rosser and Williams, 1982) and the US quality of well-being scale (Kaplan 1988). Both provide a numerical measure of health status or quality of life between zero (worst state, or dead) and one (best state, or perfect health).

The Rosser matrix combines measures of physical and social functioning with assessment of the psycho-social state of the individual to produce a health status score before and after an intervention. Each individual receives a health status score according to the disability–distress category they are placed in (the matrix contains 29 categories).

Similarly, the well-being scale of Kaplan integrates three sub-scales representing mobility, physical activity and social activity. The main difference from the Rosser based QALY is that the individual is initially ascribed a health status value of one, which is then reduced in accordance to any negative scores received on the three sub-scales. In addition, fine distinctions between health status values are claimed to be possible due to the use of a further 'negative weighting' for 22 specific health symptoms such as headaches, lisps and wearing contact lenses (Kaplan and Anderson 1988).

Both scales can be used to derive a value for the quality adjusted benefits of increased life expectancy which may be achieved through health promotion. For example, a group of individuals may be 'healthy' (i.e. assume this means they have a score of one) for their first 50 years, but have some social disability for the next five years and be bedridden for a further five years prior to death. Although death is at age 60, adjustments have to be made to the quality of life over the 10 years of disability so that quality adjusted life expectancy lies somewhere below 60 years, but above 50 years (according to the calculation using the health scales). The difference is the reduction in the well-being or quality of life of an individual. A health promotion intervention at age 40 for these individuals may result ultimately in an average delay of the onset of serious disability by 10 years, so that the group is relatively 'healthy' (for example, with a health status score of 0.7) up to age 60 and then suffers the same disability and mortality profile as in the no-health promotion scenario. Benefits are then achieved in terms of an increased quality adjusted life expectancy.

In this example the health promotion programme has provided an additional 10 years of life at an average quality of life score of 0.7. Multiplying 10 years by 0.7 results in an outcome of seven quality adjusted life years (QALYs) gained. A cost-effectiveness ratio for the programme can also be calculated. If the health promotion programme costs £70,000 the basic cost per QALY gained in this example is £10,000. This figure could then be compared with the cost-effectiveness ratios for other options (see chapter 8).

The use of QALYs represents a controversial approach to the measurement of health outcomes, and is still at an early stage of development in terms of their practical application for evaluating the output of alternative health programmes. Questions have been raised over the validity of constructing a single numerical scale which can encompass all dimensions of health status (Carr-Hill, 1989). In addition, each of the health status scales currently available employ a different method of calculation which makes comparisons between the results they produce difficult. A team of researchers have attempted to produce a 'gold standard' quality of life measure for Europe known as the EuroQol (EuroQol Group, 1990). However, this has also been criticized as being too simplistic to provide a comprehensive summary measure of health status (Carr-Hill, 1992).

Currently, there are several other problems in using QALY measures. For example, existing methods provide an assessment of the average health status for an individual or group over time but are age-independent, that is, they attribute the same value to a specific health benefit for a 70-year-old as for a 20-year-old (Loomes and McKenzie, 1989).

Cribb and Haycox (1989) have criticized health status measures such as QALYs, as being too insensitive for use in evaluating health promotion effectiveness. They argue that this is due to their inclusion of a large and indeterminant number of variables, the lower reliability of the perceived values generated and an inability to allow for the cumulative health impact over time of behavioural modification. This sensitivity argument is particularly important. The single numerical scales suffer from being bounded by 0 and 1 which reduces the possibility that individuals already high up on the scale will record actual health gains (i.e. through an improvement in quality of life) from exposure to a health promotion intervention.

Health gains may only be relevant for individuals at a lower point on the scale. Higgins (1988) argued that health promotion tends to be under-used relative to medical treatment because it is often directed at healthy people who, for example, happen to eat a high fat diet but show no signs of ill health. They tend to place a lower absolute valuation on achieving additional health gains from behavioural change compared to the value that unwell individuals requiring medical treatment place on improvements in their health. However, these do not represent very strong arguments against using measures of final outcome, but serve as reasons for directing more effort to improving their sensitivity and reliability in estimating changes in health status.

A second general set of health status measures are those which do not explicitly take account of the quality of life or physio-social benefits of reduced morbidity. One example is disability free life expectancy which provides an index of a population's health status using estimates of mortality and disability (Sullivan, 1971). One drawback to this approach is that whilst an increasing standardization and reliability of physical disability measures have been achieved in recent years, there has been less progress on developing a measure of healthy life expectancy which adequately incorporates psycho-social disability (Robine and Ritchie, 1991).

Outcome measures with only one health dimension can be used to assess the relative effectiveness of health promotion interventions. In general this relates to the use of either mortality measures (e.g.

standardized mortality rates, life years gained/saved) or morbidity measures (e.g. hospital bed-days, number of GP consultations). Most evaluations of health promotion have calculated mortality reduction outcomes because of its simplicity and greater data availability. However, this measure is inappropriate for interventions which have a greater relative impact on morbidity or quality of life. Some relatively sophisticated physical well-being or morbidity scales have been produced (Kind, 1988), for example, the sickness impact profile which assesses the impact of disease on behavioural functioning (Bergner, Babbitt and Kressel 1981), and the Nottingham health profile (Hunt *et al.*, 1980).

The discussion above has outlined several general health outcome measures that could be adopted. An alternative approach is to use a disease specific measure (Kaplan 1988). For example, the effectiveness of a multi-risk factor health promotion intervention on coronary heart disease mortality and morbidity could be measured using disease specific measures (e.g. potential life years saved from prevented heart disease or a coronary heart disease quality of life measure). This, however, represents an incomplete evaluation for two reasons. Firstly, a disease specific measure does not take account of the impact of the health promotion intervention on the prevention of other diseases. In a multi-risk factor intervention a reduction in smoking, obesity, salt intake and other such risk factors is likely to have an impact on the prevention of several diseases and not only coronary heart disease. In this context, disease specific measures may underestimate the total health gain impact of health promotion.

Secondly, the use of a disease specific measure does not take account of an increased probability of acquiring some other disease due to the problem of competing disease risks (Schaapveld *et al.*, 1990). This refers to a situation in which a successful intervention prevents the early onset of specific diseases but as people live longer there is a greater probability of acquiring other diseases than would otherwise have been expected. In this case the use of a disease specific measure could be expected to over-estimate the total health gains from a health promotion intervention compared to that which would be generated from a general outcome measure such as total life years gained.

If the overall health impact is the important outcome, then a general health measure is the most appropriate to use in an assessment of the impact of a health promotion intervention. A disease specific approach tends to have most relevance for assessing health status change over a short time period among relatively young age groups, and for conditions which have relatively high morbidity (and low mortality) such as mental illness and diabetes.

7.3 Choice of outcome measure

The appropriate outcome measure for comparisons between alternative health promotion options depends on the objective and scope of the evaluation and the aims of the options included in the analysis. For example, a comparison of the cost-effectiveness of a smoking cessation mass media campaign with a local community based promotion, with both options aimed at smoking cessation among adults, could use changes in smoking prevalence as the intermediate outcome measure to assess their relative effectiveness.

Although the two options both focus on smoking cessation, they may each have very different practical objectives. For example, the primary aim of the mass media campaign could be 'agenda setting', whilst behaviour change (i.e. actual smoking cessation) may be the primary objective of the community based initiative. In this case, if changes in smoking prevalence are to be used to assess relative effectiveness, appropriate option comparisons to adopt would be combined mass media and local promotion versus local promotion only. This would enable assessment of the additional costs and effects of using mass media to raise awareness of the issues surrounding smoking behaviour.

If mass media is viewed as an attempt to increase awareness of the risks of lung cancer and heart disease from smoking then it would be more appropriate to directly compare it with an alternative method of 'awareness raising' (e.g. leaflets in a GP surgery). In this case demand process indicators could be used to compare the relative effectiveness of each option for increasing the health knowledge of the general public or target group.

The important point is that the choice of outcome measure should not be considered in isolation from other elements of an economic evaluation. Consideration must be given to study objectives (which depends on the perspective adopted) and the choice of appropriate options (which depends on their purpose).

7.4 The relationship between the outcome measures and evaluation costs

The use of composite health status measures such as quality adjusted life years provides the greatest scope for the comparison of results from economic evaluations of health promotion programmes. For example, the health benefits of a mass media campaign for HIV infection can be directly compared with the health benefits of health education for a different at-risk group such as smokers or the young. In addition, the use of such general health status measures could also assist decisions regarding for resource allocation between curative, preventive and health promotion policies by ranking cost per quality adjusted life years results derived from a wide range of studies (Russell 1986). However, unless the same methods have been employed, the extent to which wider comparisons between health promotion and curative strategies can be made is limited.

Difficulties exist with the measurement of changes in quality of life. For example, it might be predicted that individuals exposed to a community health promotion campaign will 'feel better' from the subsequent adoption of a low fat diet and the uptake of more exercise. The collection of data to examine this proposition is likely to require the use of a questionnaire based survey, which can be costly, and the use of a general quality of life instrument. Although many such instruments exist (see Kind, 1988), none are currently able to reliably assess actual gains in quality of life due to health promotion because of the subjective and context-specific nature of this concept.

The direct measurement of the effectiveness of a health promotion intervention using final health outcomes can be costly and cover a long time period. The health benefits of a reduced incidence of disease related to health promotion often occur in the distant future. In many cases, the time lag between behavioural change and predicted disease incidence is large and uncertain and any study would have to span several decades in order to identify a possible causal relationship, such as the Framingham heart study in the USA (Dawber, 1980). A prospective study is necessary to follow through a cohort of individuals from the time of the intervention until death (or at least up to the time at which the intervention can have no further impact on health outcomes).

Several studies evaluating the effect of community based health promotion have used quasi-experimental study designs to examine changes in the incidence of heart disease related mortality among the intervention population compared to a reference population, but have only found small (and usually statistically insignificant) differences in trends. One such study was the North Karelia project in Finland in which heart disease mortality in the intervention area (North Karelia) was compared with the trend for the rest of Finland (Koskela and Puska, 1987). Although the overall trend in the incidence of heart disease mortality was downwards, no genuine difference could be detected between the intervention and reference populations after five years and only small differences after 10 years of the trial. This finding is similar to that found from other heart disease prevention studies covering less than 10 years such as the Stanford Five Cities programme in California (Farquhar *et al.*, 1990). From this evidence it appears that 5–10 years is an insufficient follow-up period for reliably assessing the prevention impact of many health promotion programmes.

A more pragmatic and less costly approach than undertaking a long-term cohort study is to measure changes in health behaviour or risk factor prevalence (i.e. use intermediate outcome and process measures) and use available epidemiological evidence to predict impacts on final health outcomes. Predictions of life years gained and age specific mortality ratio changes due to behavioural change (such as a reduction in smoking prevalence) or associated physiological change (due to lower cholesterol levels) can be attempted using epidemiological models such as PREVENT (Gunning-Schepers, 1989) or life-table analysis (St Leger, 1989).

However, there are several difficulties in using such an approach:

1. There exists a high degree of uncertainty associated with the relationship between risk factor modification and disease outcome and between behavioural change and physiological impact. Models such as PREVENT incorporate only a limited range of epidemiological associations for which relatively good data (on relative risks) exists in the literature. It cannot, for example, be used to predict the health outcome of an increase in water fluoridation, or an increase in levels of fitness from increased exercise. Even some of the associations predicted in the model have a high degree of epidemiological uncertainty, as for example between obesity and breast cancer.

2. Few health promotion interventions have a direct effect on health behaviour or risk factor prevalence that can be readily fitted into models such as PREVENT. For example, community development initiatives might result in an increase in 'informed health choice' or reduced social deprivation for some people and indices could be derived to measure this. However, to translate this to health behaviour modification or final health outcomes (for instance by using PREVENT) is not currently possible. Existing epidemiological models which examine the association between risk factor prevalence and health outcomes are not particularly appropriate for assessing the effectiveness of such progressive health promotion and education initiatives.

3. PREVENT and similar models provide simulations of the potential change in mortality only. (It includes measures such as actual and potential life years saved and absolute mortality reduction.) There is a lack of available epidemiological data for assessing accurately the morbidity consequences of behavioural change. A model which could predict mortality and morbidity outcomes would represent progress. However, even better would be to devise a method for predicting quality of life outcomes. A wide range of health promotion (and non-health promotion) options could be assessed if it was possible to derive simulations of their potential impact on short-term and future quality of life or well-being. This approach would, for example, be appropriate for assessing the effectiveness of interventions which have a direct influence on health behaviour and other interventions which increase the level of 'informed health choice' in a community.

Figure 10 outlines the trade-off between the cost of evaluation and the scope and reliability of estimates of final health outcomes. If a model such as PREVENT is used instead of a long term prospective study, a reduction in the cost of evaluation is likely to be achieved at the cost of a greater uncertainty in the precision of the final health outcome estimates.

The scope of the study could be limited to the collection of data for intermediate outcomes. However, this approach does not necessarily represent a *low* cost evaluation. For example, a large number of surveys over a five year period were required as part of the Heartbeat Wales demonstration programme in an attempt to measure change in health behaviour among the intervention population (Nutbeam and Catford, 1987).

Ideally a baseline survey on individuals' health behaviour and attitudes should be undertaken, followed-up with surveys of awareness of health education programmes and individuals' attitudinal and behavioural change subsequent to a health education intervention (Figure 10). In addition, a sufficient time period has to be allowed for behavioural change to occur, in particular to allow for relapses in behaviour (e.g. those who only give up smoking for a short period after a national 'No-Smoking Day') and for the new behaviour to filter through to others. This last point is very important for assessing the overall impact of health promotion. For example, a change in health behaviour by one group of individuals (e.g.

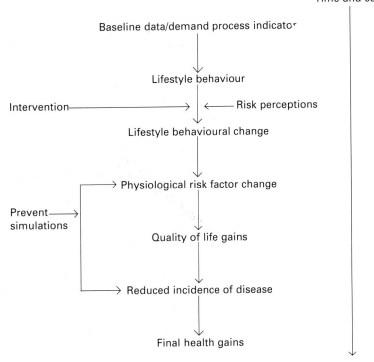

Figure 10. The outcome evaluation process.

employees), such as a change from drinking full fat to semi-skimmed milk, may subsequently be adopted by family members, neighbours and others in the community. In this way a threshold point may be reached beyond which rapid change may occur due to the new behaviour becoming the social norm.

If insufficient data exists on the intermediate outcomes of different health promotion options it may be possible instead to examine process using process indicators and make various assumptions about the link between these and intermediate outcomes. As is demonstrated in Figure 10, evaluation cost is minimized but with an even greater level of uncertainty associated with the outcome estimates. It is very difficult to derive an accurate estimate of the likely association between process indicators (e.g. the number of healthy eating leaflets distributed, the population coverage of the leaflet, the level of awareness by individuals and an understanding of the health education messages on the leaflet), and actual behavioural change. An accurate assessment of the risk perceptions of individuals exposed to the intervention, the permanency of any behavioural change and the impact of other factors on health behaviour would be necessary for reliable predictions of intermediate outcomes (which could then be used for final outcome simulations using models such as PREVENT).

7.5 Cumulative impact on health behaviour

In many cases each type of health promotion option, such as a mass media campaign, the provision of exercise facilities, lobbying for changes in social policy that has a bearing on health, do not operate as independent influences on health behaviour at any one moment in time.

In actual settings, the impact on behaviour of health promotion activities instigated in one year cannot be isolated from the impact of similar interventions operated in the previous year. Hence current health education programmes may have the objective of reinforcing messages and ensuring a greater chance of permanency in behaviour change derived from any previous health education initiatives.

In any one year the total impact of the range of health promotion interventions in a programme on health behaviour is likely to be different from that predicted by a summation of the estimated independent effects of each intervention. Such independent effects may be derived from controlled trials under experimental study conditions, but have less bearing on assessing the actual cumulative impact on health related behaviour of health promotion.

There is a need in economic evaluations of health promotion programmes in actual settings to consider such cumulative impacts over time and across interventions, especially if final health outcomes are used. Depending on the study objective, the preferred approach is likely to be to assess, within a demonstration programme, the costs and effects over two or more years of complete health promotion programmes (at the local or national level) consisting of several, often diverse, interventions.

8 The results of cost-effectiveness analysis

8.1 Overview – developing cost-effectiveness estimates

The final stage in the assessment of the cost-effectiveness of two or more options is to combine the costs and outcome data to produce costs per unit of outcome. Three approaches to the presentation of cost-effectiveness results can be outlined:

1. Production of a baseline ('best') estimate of the average costs per unit of outcome for each option. The costs can be presented as gross costs or net costs.
2. Assessment of the additional costs per extra unit of outcome for an expansion (or contraction) of the options.
3. Modification of the baseline estimates to allow for differences in the timing of costs and outcomes, uncertainty regarding the reliability and precision of cost and outcome estimates and the inclusion of equity objectives.

Figure 11 outlines these approaches as sequential steps (this is developed from stage G in Figure 1, chapter 2). Each step represents a progressively more detailed analysis and presentation of the results of

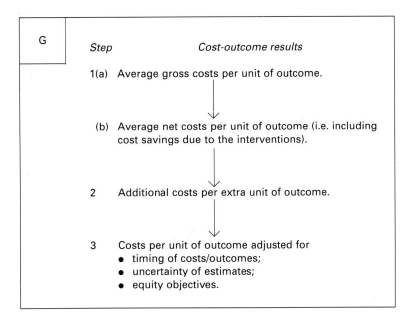

G	Step	Cost-outcome results

1(a) Average gross costs per unit of outcome.

(b) Average net costs per unit of outcome (i.e. including cost savings due to the interventions).

2 Additional costs per extra unit of outcome.

3 Costs per unit of outcome adjusted for
- timing of costs/outcomes;
- uncertainty of estimates;
- equity objectives.

Figure 11. Steps in producing cost per unit of outcome results.

an economic evaluation. A basic evaluation might involve only the first step with the aim of improving the accuracy of a baseline estimate without introducing more sophisticated analysis. However, all evaluations that recommend an option as most cost-effective on the basis of a single cost per unit of outcome comparison must be treated with caution and the methods closely examined.

Each of the steps outlined in Figure 11 are discussed more fully in Sections 8.2–8.5. Section 8.6 completes the chapter by looking at one debate. This has been given particular attention in the literature – the question of whether prevention and health promotion save future health care resources.

8.2 Results I – baseline estimates of average costs per unit of outcome

The production of average gross cost per unit of outcome estimates (e.g. cost per life year saved, cost per 1% reduction in smoking prevalence) for each option provides a baseline cost-effectiveness ratio against which the results from further, more detailed, analysis can be compared. It represents a 'best estimate' given the data available, the assumptions used to derive costs and outcomes and the judgement of the analyst.

The production of net costs per unit of outcome estimates represent a more thorough approach to the presentation of the cost-effectiveness results which requires the adoption of a societal perspective. This also provides a baseline 'best estimate' but incorporates within the costing the impact of potential savings to society (e.g. the impact and health promotion on health costs or increased work productivity). In general, this requires the corresponding use of a final health outcome measure such as quality adjusted life years to measure effectiveness. Furthermore, other costs and benefits that cannot be valued in monetary terms or are not incorporated into a quantitative health status measure can be identified and noted as qualitative evidence alongside the cost-effectiveness results. For example, the corporate image benefits to the company of a workplace health promotion initiative can be listed as additional information alongside the presentation of the net costs per quality adjusted life year gained estimates.

8.3 Results II – additional costs per unit of outcome

Often the decision facing policy makers is not which health programme to adopt, such as a prevention or a treatment strategy, but how to allocate resources efficiently between existing programmes. Help with deciding on the appropriate scale and scope of a health promotion programme can be obtained by doing an assessment of the additional costs incurred for each additional unit of outcome if the programme is expanded, or the cost reduction from a contraction of the programme (this is known in economic evaluation as marginal cost-effectiveness analysis). For example, community-based heart disease health promotion programmes (such as Look After Your Heart in England) usually consist of several types of intervention. An assessment of the marginal cost-effectiveness of expanding the programme to include an 'Eat Healthy Food' day would involve the calculation of the additional expected benefits, for example a predicted reduction in heart disease mortality, and the additional costs of the new promotion. As an example 100 additional life years might be predicted for the intervention population at an additional cost of £200 per life year saved. This can then be compared with the additional costs per extra life year saved from expanding an alternative programme.

This type of analysis can be useful for comparing two (or more) health promotion strategies which have the same objective but where one option has a lower cost and lower level of overall effectiveness than the other. Assessment of the additional costs per extra unit of outcome generated by the more costly option can assist policy makers in decisions as to whether the additional benefits are worth the extra costs (an additional important factor in this decision is who actually bears the costs and what perspective is being adopted for the evaluation).

The acceptance of baseline average cost per unit of outcome results as evidence of cost-effectiveness can be misleading. For example, a study which examined (from the perspective of the health authority) the cost-effectiveness of using different health professionals to screen hospital in-patient admissions for risk of alcohol related problems found that the average cost per positive case detected was slightly greater for nurses screening (£1.29) compared to screening by a specialist alcohol worker (£1.20) (Tolley and Rowland, 1991). On the basis of these figures alone the evidence seems to suggest that the alcohol worker is the relatively more cost-effective option. However, when the additional costs and positive case rates of each option were examined it was found that the alcohol worker detected an additional 47 cases at an additional cost of £1.04 per case. Using this data the policy maker would need to decide whether the additional cases detected by the alcohol worker was worth the additional resources required for this option. The interpretation of cost-effectiveness depends on several factors including the judgement of the decision maker, outcome targets and budget limits. Marginal cost-effectiveness analysis can assist in this decision-making process.

There is little evidence of the use of this approach in evaluations of the cost-effectiveness of health promotion/prevention interventions. Cummings, Rubin and Oster (1989) in their study of the cost-effectiveness of health education for smoking cessation in a primary care setting also included an assessment of the additional costs and effects on smoking prevalence of a follow-up visit for further advice. None of the evaluations of community-based coronary heart disease prevention/health promotion, such as the North Karelia and Minnesota programmes (Koskela and Puska, 1987; Mittlemark *et al.*, 1988), have collected adequate cost data to assess the marginal cost effectiveness of each of the major elements of the programmes.

It is very difficult to identify the specific effect on outcomes of each component of a community-based intervention without a strictly controlled experimental study design. Even if such a design were feasible, there are difficulties in determining an appropriate ordering for implementing the programme components in order to assess the change in outcomes. Local self-help groups may have little additional impact on cumulative smoking behaviour in a community when added as the tenth component, but a very large impact if included as the third component. Evidence of the independent effect of each component and interactions between components would be required to examine marginal cost-effectiveness within a health promotion programme.

8.4 Results III – timing of costs and outcomes

A general behavioural principle used in economic analysis is that people or agencies prefer to delay costs but wish to obtain immediate benefits. Hence, future benefits and costs should have a lower valuation compared to current benefits and costs. This is known as time preference and explains why, for example, consumers may prefer to pay for a washing machine using interest-free credit or will only deposit their money in a restricted access savings account if a high rate of interest is paid on the sum. In the context of health behaviour, current smoking and drinking habits of individuals may reflect their preference to enjoy these activities now at the potential cost of an increased risk of illness in the future.

Similarly, for health programmes, account has to be taken of differences in the timing of costs and outcomes. The method normally used in economic evaluations is to determine a proportionate rate that would reflect time preferences for programme costs and expected health benefits. This rate (if chosen to reflect the preferences of society) is called the social discount rate. In most studies that undertake discounting a standard rate of between 3% and 10% per annum is adopted.

The choice of discount rate is important for those health promotion and prevention interventions for which there are certain and immediate costs but which only produce health benefits in the distant future. An example of this might be a dietary campaign among school children for which effectiveness is measured by the expected reduction in future incidence of coronary heart disease. If future health benefits are valued at a lower rate than current benefits, the cost-effectiveness of such health promotion programmes will be reduced relative to curative treatment strategies for which the benefits are more immediate (Russell, 1986).

There has been much debate among health economists as to the appropriate method for dealing with health benefits that will occur in the future. Some empirical evidence has been produced that supports the view that individuals have a limited preference for health benefits now rather than in the future (Cairns, 1991). In addition, uncertainty of future health benefits represents another argument in favour of a progressively reduced valuation over time for these potential benefits (i.e. the use of a positive discount rate). There are several counter arguments against valuing future health benefits at a lower rate, such as its being unethical and based on invalid arguments (Coyle and Tolley, 1992). For example, the decision of individuals to smoke and drink may be related to a low perceived risk of ill health from this behaviour rather than a stated preference to indulge now and pay later, in terms of a reduction in future health status.

Recently, the UK Department of Health has recommended that all new economic studies of health programmes should include the principle of valuing future health benefits at the same rate as current health benefits, that is use a zero discount rate (Parsonage and Neuberger, 1992). This could have important implications for the cost-effectiveness of health promotion and prevention.

There are at least two approaches that could be adopted to address the problem of the timing of the costs and outcomes of a health promotion programme.

Firstly, more attention could be given to assessing the short-run health benefits of health promotion, for instance by focusing on the current quality of life or well-being benefits of alternative interventions. This would reduce reliance on the use of single dimension mortality and/or morbidity outcome measures for comparing programmes.

Secondly, analysis of the sensitivity of predicted health outcomes to different assumptions about the timing of costs and benefits should be undertaken. This is likely to be undertaken as part of a similar assessment of the importance of other uncertain variables on the reliability of the cost-effectiveness results. If the use of different assumptions produces a large variation in the results then it may be best to adopt a different approach. For example, if the use of assumptions of a lower valuation of future health benefits (e.g. by adopting a 5% discount rate) and an equal valuation for current and future health benefits (a 0% discount rate) for calculating the quality adjusted life years of a smoking cessation programme produced greatly diverging results, it may be better to restrict analyses to the use of current quality of life/well-being assessments, or collect better data. If the variation using different assumptions is relatively small then further deliberation regarding the appropriate valuation of future health benefits is less likely to be worth the effort involved.

Epidemiological associations between risk factors and health status represent a further area of uncertainty that may need to be addressed in the assessment of the cost-effectiveness of health promotion. This can also be incorporated by testing the sensitivity of the results to various assumptions regarding the association between intermediate outcomes and final health outcomes.

8.5 Results III – equity issues

The issue of equity and a reduction in health inequalities has been given little attention in previous economic evaluations of preventive and health promotion programmes (Cohen and Henderson 1988). However, health promotion has an important part to play in raising the health status of individuals, groups and nations above a minimum acceptable level and in turn reduce health disparities. The pursuit of efficiency objectives has been claimed by economists to lead to a potential conflict with equity objectives (Culyer 1980). This view has resulted in the use of economic evaluation to assess whether or not an intervention produces the greatest aggregate health benefit at the least cost, and the issue of whether this benefit has been equitably distributed is consigned to being a secondary concern.

In the context of health promotion and prevention this approach is inadequate as it is not possible to simply and clearly separate equity and efficiency objectives in the promotion of health in society. It is possible for an equitable health promotion programme to also be an efficient programme, and conversely for an inequitable programme to be inefficient. Whitehead and Dahlgren (1991) provide an example of this possibility in relation to the setting of targets for the uptake of cervical screening.

They argue that uptake rates as high as 90% might not achieve the desired output in terms of reduced mortality if the higher risk of cervical cancer exists among the 10% who are not screened. Such a programme might therefore be inefficient and inequitable as the people in the early stages of cervical cancer who could benefit most from screening are not screened.

A preventive strategy which focuses on equity of health would ensure targets are set to reflect the higher prevalence of disease among relatively disadvantaged social groups (Whitehead and Dahlgren 1991). An increase in total health benefit would result from more effective targeting of activities, such as cervical screening according to need (with need taken to reflect a higher risk of ill health or disease). If there is no corresponding increase in costs then the programme would serve to reduce health inequalities and increase efficiency. If costs and health benefits are increased this represents the price that has to be paid to achieve the dual objectives of a higher total level of health benefit and a more equitable distribution.

The notion of equity is multi-faceted. There are a number of definitions which are used in different contexts: equal expenditure per capita, equity according to need, equality of access, equality of access for equal need and equality of health (Mooney, 1983). Two broad equity principles which appear to be of most relevance to health promotion can be defined.

Firstly, equity of access relates to each individual having reasonable opportunity to use health promoting facilities, such as leisure centres, supermarkets selling low fat food products, or to gain access to health promotion initiatives (e.g. physical activity programmes, screening facilities). Achieving equity of access involves consideration of the potential time and money costs incurred by individual and the constraints this places on he or she gaining access to health promoting facilities. The processes involved in the provision of health promotion are important in determining equity of access.

Notions such as 'equity of access for equal need' or 'equity of use for equal need' can be incorporated within a broad second principle – that of equity of health. 'Need' for health promotion can be related to the risk associated to health from, for example, the interrelationships between social environment, dietary patterns and smoking prevalence. Health education could then be used as an instrument to encourage social policy aimed at reducing socio-economic and health inequalities in society, or targeted at those work environments which are associated with higher health risks (e.g. related to smoking patterns).

For the purposes of an economic evaluation, equity objectives need to be clearly defined and incorporated. It is appropriate for an evaluation of a health promotion programme aimed at preventing coronary heart disease to have as a starting point a predefined equity objective, such as improving the diet of communities living in socially deprived localities. Alternative methods of providing dietary health education targeted at these social groups could then be compared to determine the most cost-effective option for achieving health benefits and reducing health inequalities across groups in society.

8.6 Impact of health promotion on health care costs

A significant area of debate among economists has been the issue of the effect of prevention and health promotion on future health care costs (Kristein 1977, Warner 1979, Rogers, Eaton and Bruhn, 1981, Shephard 1985, Russell 1986, Higgins 1988). The actual impact is uncertain but is important for the production of net cost per unit of outcome results.

The conventional wisdom has been that prevention saves future health care expenditure, although the opposite relationship of an increase in health care costs has, in the last 10–15 years, become the more popular viewpoint among economists. However, there is little substantive evidence available to support either assertion. Most actual evaluations have predicted the impact of the potential medical cost of prevention and health promotion using less than ideal data. For example, St Leger (1989) in the UK used hospital daily bed use as a proxy for hospital costs and applied this to life expectancy data (using life tables) for males in England and Wales. He predicted the impact on health care costs of reductions of 30% in the prevalence of ischaemic heart disease and all forms of cancers, and the complete cessation of smoking and cases of injury and poisoning. Despite these being unrealistic prevention scenarios, only in the latter category were any future medical care cost savings predicted.

In addition, a study by Weinkam, Rosenbaum and Sterling (1987) using life expectancy estimates and data on hospital usage taken from the 1970 US National Health Interview Survey, predicted that complete smoking cessation by smokers in the sample would not result in any significant medical cost savings. Somewhat paradoxically they predicted that male smokers aged 44 years and over and female smokers aged 38 years and over would experience fewer remaining lifetime hospital days compared to non-smokers in the sample. Warner (1987) has argued that the economic benefits of a tobacco free society in the US are relatively modest but that the main benefits are in terms of an improvement in the nation's health and hence quality and quantity of life. He claimed the commercial justification for not encouraging smoking cessation – that jobs in the tobacco industry would be lost – is misconceived on two grounds. Firstly, these jobs could be redistributed to other sectors of the economy (debateable if the economy has high unemployment). Secondly, smoking cessation education could be justified in terms of the potential social and economic benefits of removing the 350,000 annual excess deaths in the US due to tobacco smoking.

A number of economic studies have assessed the impact on costs of a more active lifestyle, for example through increased exercise. In the US, studies by Shephard (1985) and Keeler et al. (1989) have predicted potential cost savings, whilst Hatziandreu et al. (1988) concluded that exercise does not result in a cost reduction. Shephard (1985) claimed that empirical evidence up to the time of his study demonstrated that the potential direct and indirect medical and economic cost savings from routine exercise could be expected to exceed the extra costs of treating sports injuries, related time off work and for child care to participate in exercise programmes. Keeler *et al.* (1989), using a regression model, estimated a total lifetime cost estimate for a sedentary lifestyle of $4,000 to $27,000 per person (1988 US prices). In a regression with an active exercise variable replacing the sedentary lifestyle variable Keeler *et al*, estimated a potential savings of between $1,900 to $9,300 per person.

Russell (1984, 1986) has argued that prevention needs to be justified on the grounds of providing improvements in health status for individuals at an extra cost. She argued that in each situation in which a choice exists, the costs and benefits of prevention should be compared with the costs and benefits of curative policies to determine which provides the best health investment. Shephard, in a debate on the issue with Russell has claimed that more evidence is needed on the relative cost-effectiveness of prevention/health promotion and curative strategies (Shephard, 1987; Russell, 1987a). Shephard argued that health promotion and prevention provided the greatest potential for improvements in economic productivity and quality of life outcomes in the US.

9 Applying the economic evaluation framework – case studies

9.1 Overview – case study criteria

The previous chapters have examined in detail a framework for the economic evaluation of health promotion. This framework has two main applications:

1. Retrospective. As a framework to assess the coverage and quality of previous studies of the cost-effectiveness of health promotion interventions.
2. Prospective. To provide guidelines for the development of actual evaluations of the cost-effectiveness of health promotion interventions.

This chapter will focus on a retrospective use of the framework, applying it to three case study areas:

1. Exercise/diet interventions.
2. Smoking cessation health education.
3. Workplace health promotion.

The aim of the case studies is to demonstrate to health promotionalists and other non-economists the possibilities of using the framework to assess the content and quality of published studies which claim to examine the cost-effectiveness of health promotion and to promote an understanding of this literature. This also provides a useful basis for the application of the framework to prospective studies. This is being developed in a separate paper focusing on health promotion for coronary heart disease (Godfrey, Hardman and Tolley, 1992).

Three general criteria for the choice of case study areas and the inclusion of studies in this review have been adopted:

1. A pragmatic approach. The studies reviewed, therefore, are illustrative of the type of evaluation that has been carried out to date rather than examples of 'best practice'. Areas in which several papers have been published (e.g. smoking cessation, workplace) or studies which provide interesting examples of the use of cost-effectiveness analysis (e.g. a study by Toevs, Kaplan and Atkins, 1984, discussed in case study group A) have been included. Each of the published studies in the review includes at least one option which can be defined as 'health education'.
2. The studies have undertaken a complete cost-effectiveness or cost-benefit analysis and not simply an assessment of the efficacy or effectiveness of alternative health promotion interventions.
3. The evaluations cover interventions in developed countries. No attempt has been made to assess studies of health promotion

interventions in less developed countries. The design of economic evaluations in these countries face a different set of social, economic and cultural circumstances which are not within the scope of this report.

9.2 Evaluation criteria

The studies reviewed in this chapter are examined using the components of the economic evaluation framework discussed in chapters 1 to 8.

The potential contribution of the economic evaluation case studies can also be assessed in terms of the extent to which, as a group of studies, they provide useful information on cost-effective health education/promotion interventions from a societal perspective and so help inform social and economic policy making. Three summary criteria – scope, generalizability and comparability – are used for this purpose. The interpretation of these concepts is provided in Figure 12.

Scope relates to the options and objectives of economic evaluations of health promotion options. To date, the focus of economic evaluation has been directed at assessments of the cost-effectiveness of primary and secondary prevention initiatives such as immunization and screening. Very little attention has been given by economists to evaluating the cost-effectiveness of alternative health education programmes or health education compared with other strategies, such as treatment and care. In two volumes of over 200 case studies of the economic evaluation of health programmes, only one study was included which had incorporated an assessment of the cost-effectiveness of a health education intervention (see Drummond, 1981; Drummond *et al.*, 1987).

Generalizability concerns the relevance of the study results beyond the specific setting and is dependent on study design. For example, the cost savings estimated in many of the workplace health

---

Scope

Have the studies considered a wide range of health education and health promotion options?

Have the studies focused on disease prevention and/or well-being objectives?

Generalizability

Have the studies achieved a good balance between internal and external validity through their study design.

Comparability

Are the results of the study comparable? Have they used similar methods for deriving costs and outcomes?

Figure 12. Criteria for assessing evaluations of health promotion.

promotion evaluations carried out in the US may not be relevant for the UK context because of the different factors affecting costs and outcomes in each country. The study design has an important bearing on the generalizability of results. Health promotion evaluations that have used a randomized experimental design have relatively less 'generalizability' than those which have used quasi-experimental designs.

Comparability represents the extent to which the results from different studies can be compared. This depends on scope and generalizability considerations but also on the variations in the methods used for measuring costs and outcomes in different studies. One approach to improving comparability is to produce a checklist of standard costing and outcome measurement methods to which all new cost-effectiveness evaluations should adhere. Russell (1986) has argued that the cost-effectiveness analysis framework provides opportunities for more standardized health promotion/ prevention evaluation methodology and hence comparability of results.

Studies included in each of the case study areas are reviewed in the remainder of this chapter. The sub-headings used represent each of the components of an economic evaluation.

9.3 Case study A – diet/exercise health education

Three US studies are assessed in this case study group.

Study

Kaplan, R.M., Atkins, C.J. and Wilson, D.K. (1988). The cost-utility of diet and exercise interventions in non-insulin dependent diabetes mellitus. *Health Promotion*, **2** (4) 331–40.

Problem definition, objectives and options

The study problem was to examine the cost-effectiveness of the use of alternative health promotion interventions for improving the health status of non-insulin dependent diabetes mellitus patients. The perspective adopted was not clearly stated in the paper, although implicitly an attempt appears to have been made to adopt the perspective of society (due to the use of a general health outcome measure). However, as the costs incurred by patients or the community were not included, the actual perspective appears to be that of the health service. The general objective was to identify efficiency in achieving quality of life benefits from diet/exercise health education and behavioural change programmes. The economic objective was to determine the additional cost per well-year of this intervention relative to a usual care/education package.

The options included were a 10-week health education programme for diabetes care compared to diet/exercise health education with subsequent health support in the form of a five-week diet modification programme and a five-week fitness programme. As this was targeted at patients with diabetes, the interventions represent tertiary stage health education measures.

Study design

The intervention group received health education and diet/fitness programmes and the control group received only diabetes care education. This experimental study design was possible because it was small scale and had a clearly defined target group. A total of 76 patients were randomly allocated to the intervention and control groups with changes in well-being assessed at 3-, 6-, 12- and 18-month periods after the programme had finished.

Costs and outcomes

A numerical scale final health outcome measure was used to evaluate the effectiveness of the interventions. This was the quality of well-being scale devised by Bush, Chen and Patrick (1973), which was used to produce estimates of 'well-years' generated (i.e. life expectancy adjusted for expected quality of life). Although this produces a measure of the benefit of diet/exercise health education and health support for individuals with diabetes (and hence implies a social perspective), only the direct costs to the health agencies have been calculated (e.g. for physical examinations, education provision, ECG evaluations, the behaviour modification programmes, medical supervision). The costs of time and money incurred by patients from participation in the programmes should also have been included.

   The costs were calculated using 1986 average clinical charges for several procedures used in the interventions. This provides only a very crude approximation of the actual costs of the health promotion programmes. The reliability of the cost estimates could have been improved if data had been collected on actual resource use of the patients with diabetes.

Results

The study produced a baseline result over the 18-month period for the diet/exercise programme of $10,870 per additional well-year (in 1987 US dollars) relative to basic diabetes care education. The authors argued that allowance for differential timing was inappropriate as both 'costs and benefits were evaluated in the short term'. However, the impact on the cost-effectiveness results of an assumption that the effects (well-being gains) occur only at the end of an 18-month follow-up period was tested. Discount rates of 5% and 10% were used to reflect a lower valuation after 18 months of the health benefits, resulting in cost per additional well-year estimates of $11,690 to $12,500. The authors concluded that due to the short time period covered, the analysis was not particularly sensitive to assumptions about the differential timing and valuation of benefits. Large variations in other assumptions, such as a lower level of estimated health benefit from the intervention, had only a relatively small impact on the results.

The authors compared their results with cost per well-year results produced for other health care interventions and concluded that 'investments in behavioural interventions (for non-insulin dependent diabetes mellitus patients) produce benefits at a cost quite comparable to many widely advocated health care alternatives' (p. 338).

The equity implications of the results were not addressed in this paper.

Other related studies

A study by Toevs, Kaplan and Atkins (1984) used a similar approach to the Kaplan *et al.* (1988) evaluation. This involved an assessment of the cost-effectiveness of behavioural health promotion programmes for patients with chronic obstructive pulmonary disease (COPD). The same quality of well-being scale was used to measures outcome from alternative exercise-based behavioural programmes. An experimental study design was adopted. Toevs, Kaplan and Atkins (1984) produced estimates of US$10,800 to $36,900 per additional well-year for the exercise education and behaviour modification programme compared to the 'exercise education only' controls. As this is based on 1983 values – Kaplan and co-workers (1988) used 1987 values – this intervention appears not to be as cost-effective relative to the programme for the diabetes patients. This assertion would require closer examination if the evidence was being used to determine actual resource allocation decisions between such programmes.

Study (2)

Berwick, D.M., Cretin, S. and Keeler, E. (1981). Cholesterol, children and heart disease: an analysis of alternatives. *Pediatrics*, **68** (5) 721–9

Problem definition, objectives and options

The study problem was to examine the cost-effectiveness of alternative health education and prevention options for reducing cholesterol levels and probability of future heart disease among children. The perspective adopted appears to be that of the provider agencies.

The general objective of the study was the evaluation of the benefits of preventing heart disease through the use of health education/ screening among 10-year-old male children. In economic terms, the objective was to compare costs per life year saved for alternative cholesterol lowering strategies. Several options were included in the evaluation. These were (1) a high risk group option where individual education on diet was given to those children who, through screening, were found to have cholesterol levels above a specified level (2) population-based dietary health education using mass media and school-based programmes, aimed at lowering cholesterol levels among all 10-year-old children, and (3) 'doing nothing' (i.e. no screening or health education).

For the screening/health education option, several variants on the method of screening were assessed. Broadly, universal screening, in which all 10-year-old children were screened, was compared with targeted screening in which only those with a family history of heart disease (discovered through a questionnaire) were screened for high cholesterol levels.

Study design

A non-experimental study design was used to assess the effectiveness of each health education and screening option. Assumptions on the effectiveness of cholesterol reducing interventions were made and the relationship between reduced cholesterol levels and heart disease incidence was based on published epidemiological evidence. The authors could find no evidence at the time of the study on the efficacy of dietary interventions for reducing cholesterol levels but argued that the high mortality rate from heart disease warranted the adoption of such measures. It was assumed that efficacy would eventually be proven and more recent evidence appears to support this assertion (Hetzel and Berenson, 1987).

Published life expectancy tables, which take account of increased mortality from other causes if the probability of heart disease has been reduced, were used to predict the impact of the interventions on survival probability.

Costs and outcomes

The study estimated the direct cost (in 1975 US dollars) of the alternative programmes incurred by the provider agencies (although who these agencies are is not specified). This was compared with zero costs and outcomes for the 'do-nothing' option. A final health outcome measure was used. This was the total predicted life years saved from each intervention using life expectancy tables assuming various impacts of dietary change on cholesterol levels. For the universal screening and health education options it was assumed that a 10% reduction in cholesterol could, at best, be achieved, whilst only a 1–2% average reduction of cholesterol levels was predicted from the population-based intervention, although the benefits of this are spread over a greater number of people. No data was provided for the reduction in cholesterol levels for those receiving targeted screening, but it can be assumed that they were reduced to safe levels in all children screened.

Costs to the individual have not been calculated although these could be significant in terms of time and money spent on attending screening sessions. The outcome measure used implicitly incorporates the potential benefits to society of dietary health education, but by excluding costs to individuals does not attempt a full societal costing.

Results

The study used a set of predicted estimates to determine the relative cost-effectiveness of alternative screening and health education options. For this reason, the sensitivity of the results to a wide range of assumptions regarding the compliance, cost and outcome estimates was examined. The 'base-case' estimate for each option was produced assuming a lower valuation for future costs and benefits (by using a 5% discount rate). This produced a cost per life year saved for the universal screening/education intervention of $10,000 compared to $7,000 for the targeted screening/education programme. However, the mass media/school education programme appeared to be the most cost-effective at approximately $3,000 per life year saved.

Altering the discount rate to take account of different assumptions for the valuation of the future costs and benefits of each option had the largest impact on the cost-effectiveness results. This was because the savings in life years were assumed to occur 30 or more years after a reduction in cholesterol levels among the children. For example, an equal value for current and future health benefits (or a zero discount rate) reduced the costs per life year saved for the universal screening programme to between $600 to $1,000, whilst a large decrease in the value of future health benefits (10% discount rate) produced cost per life year estimates of between $83,500 to $105,000.

Berwick, Cretin and Keeler used the base-case estimates to compare their results with the estimates for cost per life year gained for health care interventions produced in other studies. Again the findings for dietary health education were favourable, although there were many difficulties in comparing such studies because of the different costing and data collection methodologies employed.

Equity issues were not addressed in this study.

Study (3)

Hatziandreu, E.I., Koplan, J.P., Weinstein, M.C. *et al.* (1988). A cost-effectiveness analysis of exercise as a health promotion activity. *American Journal of Public Health*, **78** (11), 1417–21

Problem definition, objectives and options

The study problem was broadly to estimate the health benefits and economic implications of the promotion and uptake of exercise using cost-effectiveness analysis. A society perspective was adopted, this being reflected in the costs calculated and outcome measure used. The general objective was to assess the cost-effectiveness of exercise promotion for the primary prevention of coronary heart disease. The economic objectives were to assess whether economic savings could be generated and to calculate the costs per life year gained, costs per quality adjusted life year (QALY) gained, cost per case averted and cost per death averted. The alternative option was no exercise promotion or uptake. There are likely to be costs and consequences associated with such a 'do-nothing' alternative although these were not identified in the paper.

Study design

A non-experimental study design was used by Hatziandreu *et al.* Using age-specific incidence rates drawn from the Framingham heart study (Dawber, 1980), the authors predicted the impact of exercise over a 30-year period on the survival probabilities of a hypothetical cohort of 1,000 men aged 35 years. One set of predictions were based on the cohort participating in active regular exercise (defined as jogging using over 2,000 kcal per week) after receiving health education. A second set of predictions were based on the cohort not receiving health education or undertaking any exercise.

Costs and outcomes

The estimated costs of physician-time spent providing health education on exercise to each person during a routine visit to the surgery was included. The major element of the cost assessment was that estimated for individuals through the purchase of running equipment, time spent undertaking exercise and in loss of earnings from time off work due to exercise related injury. In addition, costs to the health service and lost earnings to the individual due to premature mortality and morbidity from coronary heart disease were estimated for the exercise and no-exercise predictions.

The cost estimates were rough approximations based on various assumptions about the likely cost-related consequences of the promotion and uptake of an exercise regime. No sources for the cost estimates are given, so it is possible that they are based on the authors' 'best guestimates'.

Health outcomes, heart disease cases/deaths averted and years of life gained have been predicted using life expectancy tables and epidemiological data on the relationship between exercise and heart disease incidence. Most of the assumptions used to derive costs and outcomes were arbitrary and some appear unrealistic. An annual probability of injury of 5%, with 17% of those injured each year permanently quitting jogging, was assumed. In addition, the authors included an assumption that 10% of men exercise. This could represent the assumed effectiveness of the physician advice to undertake exercise, although this assumption does not appear to correspond with the definition of the cohort of 1,000 men as 'exercisers'. An assumption that exercise (as defined in the paper) reduces the risk of coronary heart disease by 50% was based on epidemiological evidence from one previous study. Finally, quality adjusted life years for exercise and non-exercise interventions were generated by assuming that the value in terms of quality of a year of life spent with (non-fatal) coronary heart disease was 80% (0.8) of a healthy year (1) and that time spent injured was valued by individuals at 90% (0.9) of normal health.

Results

The total predicted costs (in 1985 values) of the exercise intervention over the 30-year period was US$32 million compared to $26 million for the non-exercise simulation, the authors concluding that the 'best prediction' was that the promotion of exercise would not produce net economic savings. However, this assumed a proportion of exercise 'dislikers' among the cohort who were coerced into regular exercise participation. If exercise was only undertaken if individuals enjoyed it or had indifferent attitudes to it, then this would reduce the total cost of their time spent on this activity (due to a lower average valuation of the 'perceived cost' of time spent on exercise). This was predicted to reduce the total estimated cost for the exercise intervention to $23 million.

The cost and cost-effectiveness results were based on an assumed lower valuation for costs and benefits occuring after the first year; with a discount rate of 3% per annum used to reflect this. Four sets of cost-effectiveness results were produced: costs per quality adjusted life years gained of $11,313, cost per year of life gained of $27,851, cost per coronary heart disease death averted of $76,760 and costs per coronary heart disease case averted of $250,836.

Extensive testing of the sensitivity of the results to different assumptions was carried out. This was essential given the arbitrary methods used for deriving most of the estimates. The assumption of no reduction in the value of future costs and benefits (i.e. a zero discount rate) and a higher estimate for this reduction compared to the baseline estimate did not have a particularly large impact on the results as might have been expected. This was partially due to the small range of discount-rates used (0–5%, compared to 3% for the baseline estimate). Large variations in results were related to different assumptions for the relative risks of heart disease for non-exercisers and different assumptions regarding costs. The accuracy of the cost-effectiveness ratios depends on the validity of including the costs of time spent by individuals on exercise, injury and heart disease-related medical costs and lost earnings for exercisers and non-exercisers through injury and ill health. The authors estimated that if the potential savings in health care costs through the exercise intervention were excluded, a higher cost per quality adjusted life year of $30,500 (3% discount rate) would be predicted.

Evaluation criteria applied to the diet/exercise case studies

The economic evaluation case studies outlined above can also be assessed according to scope, generalizability and comparability criteria.

Scope

The focus of all the studies (in relation to objectives and options) is on exercise and/or diet behavioural modification. In two studies (Berwick, Cretin and Keeler, 1981; Hatziendreu *et al.*, 1988), a long-term perspective was adopted with the objective being to examine the cost-effectiveness of exercise/diet health education and health promotion for reducing future heart disease mortality and morbidity. The other study (Kaplan, Atkins and Wilson 1988) adopted a short-term perspective to assess the quality of life benefits of behavioural modification for patients with a specific 'high morbidity' disorder (diabetes). Only the Berwick, Cretin and Keeler (1981) study attempted to evaluate the cost-effectiveness of a range of health promotion or health education strategies (screening and individual counselling versus mass media/school health education).

Generalizability

The results from each study are affected by the study design adopted. Kaplan, Atkins and Wilson (1988) adopted an experimental study design producing high internal validity (i.e. under controlled scientific conditions. See section 5.3). However, as with most randomized control trials in health promotion, the effectiveness results lacked generalizability because of the study's small scale (only 76 participants), short-term perspective and the controlled setting which excluded the influence of social, organizational and other behavioural factors on the actual effectiveness of the intervention (i.e. low external validity). Whilst the non-experimental design of the other studies enabled assessment of a larger scale intervention and the adoption of a long-term perspective, they offered little in terms of an improved external validity, and demonstrated a lower internal validity compared to the experimental studies. A quasi-experimental study design involving the collection of actual data may have provided a better balance between internal and external validity for the studies reviewed here.

Comparability

All the studies used a final outcome measure which should enable comparisons with cost-effectiveness results produced for other health care interventions. Each of the studies reviewed above have attempted to place their results in a 'league table' alongside similar estimates for cost per life year, quality adjusted life year or well-years gained that have been produced in other studies for a range of preventive or treatment programmes. Unfortunately, differences across studies in the costing methods employed, specific outcome measures used and the study design reduces the reliability and validity of such comparisons.

A major limitation with all the studies in this section is the lack of attention given to the valuation of costs (which have been mostly arbitrary and based on average cost estimates), and the assumptions regarding the effectiveness of health education in achieving behavioural change. Both Kaplan, Atkins and Wilson, (1988) and Hatziandreu *et al.* (1988) assumed a certain level of effectiveness for health education in achieving behavioural change but have not adequately assessed the relative cost-effectiveness (using either process or intermediate outcome measures) of alternative health education options.

9.4 Case study B – smoking cessation health education

Several studies have examined the economic aspects of smoking and smoking cessation programmes, although the number is still small compared to studies of effectiveness. Smoking cessation health education represents one of the few areas in which some evidence of cost-effectiveness exists (Elixhauser, 1990). However, as most studies have been conducted in the US, their conclusions may not apply to other countries with different social, economic and cultural environments, such as the UK.

Two studies of the cost-effectiveness of smoking health education interventions which differ in their scope and methods used are assessed in this case study (Windsor, Warner and Cutter, 1988; Cummings, Rubin and Oster 1989). Both are from the US. In addition, a brief assessment of a paper from the UK by Williams (1987) is provided. The latter study has been very influential in demonstrating the potential use of quality adjusted life years for comparing the cost-effectiveness of health education interventions such as smoking advice with medical treatment interventions.

Study (4)

Cummings, S.R., Rubin, S.M. and Oster, G. (1989). The cost-effectiveness of counselling smokers to quit. *Journal of the American Medical Association*, **261** (1), 75–9

Problem definition, objectives and options

The study problem was to examine the cost-effectiveness of the primary prevention of ill health through smoking cessation health education provided by a physician. The rationale provided by the authors for the study was that smoking represented the most preventable cause of mortality in the US, and that prior evidence existed for the effectiveness of physician-provided health education for influencing smokers to quit.

A societal perspective was adopted, although the costs incurred by individuals were assumed to be zero. The authors cited evidence from a survey conducted in the US that over half of the smokers who visited their doctor over a one-year period received no advice to quit smoking. Thus the economic objective set was to assess the potential costs per life year saved if all smokers on a routine visit to their doctor were also provided with smoking cessation education. No alternative options were explicitly analysed in the paper, although the results were compared with evidence from other studies of the cost per life year saved for other common preventive interventions such as drug therapy for hypertension and hypocholesterolemia, and nicotine gum prescription.

Study design

The study design was non-experimental with effectiveness data for smoking cessation derived from published studies or estimated by the authors. Evidence from four randomized control trials that met the authors' inclusion criteria on the effectiveness of brief physician advice to quit smoking on quit rates was analysed. From this the authors assumed a 'base' quit rate among smokers of 2.7% after one year. The authors could find no published evidence on relapse rates following one-year cessation, so assumed a rate of 10% and no long-term health benefits for relapsers.

The health benefits of a reduced probability of ill health from quitting smoking at ages between 35 and 69 were measured using life expectancy estimates for ex-smokers from published epidemiological studies. The authors claimed their survival estimates were reliable as they were similar to that found in a study which had used Framingham heart survey data (Dawber, 1980).

Costs and outcomes

The costs of physician time to provide brief advice and the cost of the production of a self-help booklet, that was assumed would be given to patients at the same time, were estimated. These were calculated using the average charge for physician time and the authors' estimate of the cost of the self-help material. No other costs were included although the adoption of a societal perspective meant that the costs of patient time and expenses should also have been included. These costs were excluded by the authors on the basis that as advice was provided during a routine office visit, no alternative use value existed for that time. This could justify the exclusion of patients' travel expenses and time (as this would have been incurred anyway) but does not necessarily justify a zero valuation for the estimated four minutes of patient time spent receiving smoking cessation advice. Patients may (if given the choice) prefer to use that time to receive different advice, for example on diet, or a fitness check, from their doctor. If so, this time should be included in the cost estimates.

The potential costs of increased medical care from a longer life expectancy subsequent to smoking cessation were not assessed as the authors stated that any increased costs were probably offset by health care cost savings from reduced smoking-related illness.

The study used 'years of life saved' as the final health outcome measure. Only rough approximations of the health benefits were derived due to the limited amount of epidemiological data used in the study. In addition, no attempt was made to estimate morbidity reduction or quality of life benefits from an effective smoking cessation programme.

Results

An extensive set of cost per life year saved estimates were presented based on a wide range of alternative assumptions regarding quit rates, relapse rates and the current value of future health benefits (i.e. choice of discount rate). The 'base estimate' using a 2.7% one year quit rate, 10% subsequent relapse rate and a lower valuation for future health benefits (using a 5% discount rate) produced age specific (in five year bands from age 35–69) costs per life year saved of $705 to $988 for men and $1,204 to $2,058 for women (in 1984 US dollars).

The reliability of these 'best estimates' was tested by increasing the cost estimate by 50%, using quit rates of 1% and 4.4%, a relapse rate of 50% and discount rates of 3% and 7% (the assumption that future benefits have the same value as current benefits – a zero discount rate – was not considered), and several combinations of the most pessimistic assumptions.

This resulted in a wide range of cost-effectiveness results although the authors stated that even if a pessimistic assumption of a 1% quit rate among men aged 45–50 years was used, the cost per life year saved of $2,020 compared favourably with that of other preventive practices drawn from other studies (for example, $11,300 for testing moderate hypertension, $65–£108,000 for hypercholesterolemia and $4,113 for nicotine gum provided in addition to advice given by physicians).

The study attempted a limited analysis of the additional costs per extra life year saved (i.e. marginal cost-effectiveness) of a follow-up advice session. Only very tentative results were possible due to the lack of reliable published randomized control trial evidence on the effectiveness of follow up visits on quit rates. However, using the pessimistic assumption of a 1% quit rate among 45–50-year-old men, the marginal cost-effectiveness of the follow-up visit was estimated at $5,051 which, despite being higher than the initial visit, the authors claimed was still relatively cost-effective in comparison with other common preventive practices.

Study (5)

Windsor, R.A., Warner, K.E. and Cutter, G.R. (1988). A cost-effectiveness analysis of self-help smoking cessation methods for pregnant women. *Public Health Reports*, **103** (1), 83–8.

Problem definition, objectives and options

The study examined the relative cost-effectiveness of alternative health education strategies to assist pregnant women to quit smoking. The perspective adopted for the study was that of the single agency – the pre-natal clinic.

The general objective was to focus on reducing the incidence of low birth weights due to women smoking whilst pregnant. The economic objective was therefore defined as determining the method that would achieve the lowest cost and the highest quit rate.

Three health education options were defined. These were: (a) the current 'no change' strategy of providing pregnant women smokers with standard information and advice to quit smoking, (b) the provision of a general *Freedom from Smoking in 20 Days* leaflet to pregnant women smokers in addition to the standard information and advice as in option (a), and (c) the provision of a manual written for pregnant women called *A Pregnant Women's Self-Help Guide to Quit Smoking* in addition to the standard information and advice provided in option (a).

Study Design

An experimental study design was adopted for the evaluation of quit rates achieved through each option. A total of 309 pregnant smokers attending three pre-natal clinics were randomly allocated to three groups. The control group received option (a), that is, standard information and advice to quit smoking. The other two groups received, in addition to the information provided to the control group, either a general leaflet on smoking cessation or the pregnant women's manual. These represented the intervention groups. The women's smoking status was recorded on first attendance at the clinic (when health education was also provided), at mid-pregnancy and at the end of the pregnancy.

Costs and outcomes

A limited range of costs were calculated due to the narrow perspective adopted for the study. Only the costs of pre-natal clinic staff (nurses) involved in administering health education and monitoring smoking status and the costs of educational material were included. The costs of nurse time inputs were carefully calculated by multiplying the approximate average time spent on education and monitoring by the average payment rate for health department nurses. The authors accepted that other costs are likely to be incurred, for example, the client's time in receiving education and the costs of supplies for saliva thiocyanate tests (used to confirm smoking status). However, as the perspective adopted was that of the clinic, these costs were not included as they would not normally be expected to be included in the clinic budget.

The end-of-pregnancy quit rates among the control and

intervention groups provided the measure of effectiveness. This represents an intermediate outcome measure – smoking cessation was determined through self-reporting and verified by testing saliva samples. The inclusion of such a test increases costs (due to extra staff time involved). However, this has no impact on the relative cost-effectiveness of the options as this cost was incurred equally across all three groups. It may have improved the reliability of the outcome results (assuming that the testing method is reliable and accurate).

In measuring effectiveness, the criteria used in the study was complete smoking cessation by the end of the pregnancy. No attempt was made to measure effectiveness in terms of reduced levels of smoking. Although not the direct purpose of the study, no discussion was provided of the possible relationship of smoking cessation with birth weight and final health outcomes (in terms of the health status of the baby or mother).

Results

The authors concluded that option (c) – the special guide on smoking cessation for pregnant women (in addition to standard information and advice) – was most cost-effective for reducing smoking prevalence. The quit rate was 14% of all women in the group, producing a cost per 1% of quitters of $51 (price year not defined). The least cost-effective option was claimed to be the non-specialist leaflet option (b), which produced a quit rate of 6% at a cost per 1% of quitters of $119. The control intervention (option (a) – standard information and advice) produced a quit rate of 2% and a cost per 1% of quitters of $104.

A statement was made in the paper that the greater effectiveness of option (b) compared to option (a) would not compensate for the extra cost. This statement is misleading and only appears to represent the judgement of the authors. From a different perspective, such as that of, for example, the clinic manager, the higher quit rate may be thought to be worth the extra cost. Whose judgement is the most valid? A decision on cost-effectiveness might be influenced by several factors such as the desire to reach a specified outcome target (e.g. a minimum quit rate of 5%). However, option (c) in comparison with options (a) and (b) is both a lower cost and more effective intervention and so is unambiguously the most cost-effective of the strategies.

A useful extension to the study would have been an analysis of the additional costs and effects of options (b) and (c) compared to option (a), which represents a minimum baseline level of health education.

The authors attempted basic testing of the sensitivity of their cost-effectiveness results to different assumptions for costs and outcomes. For example, an estimate of the cost of clients' time spent reading and using the self-help material was included. They concluded that as little variation in results were found, their original estimates of cost-effectiveness were reliable and valid.

Study (6)

Williams, A. (1987). Screening for risk of CHD: is it a wise use of resources? In *Screening for Risk of Coronary Heart Disease*, ed. Oliver *et al.* Wiley & Sons.

A general assessment of the study

The objective of the study by Williams (1987) was to examine the health status benefits and costs of various interventions aimed at reducing risks of coronary heart disease among a hypothetical cohort of men aged 40 years or more. The health benefit measure used was quality adjusted life years. The cohort of 1000 men were assumed to have attended a GP surgery for a routine visit and were then opportunistically screened for risk factors for coronary heart disease. The author's own estimates of the average costs and predicted benefits of various interventions were used to compare the cost-effectiveness of various health education and treatment options. A cost per quality adjusted life year estimated of GP advice to stop smoking was calculated and compared with similar estimates for GP administered drug therapy to control hypertension, or to control serum cholesterol levels and several other treatment options such as coronary artery bypass grafting.

Williams concluded that GP advice to stop smoking appeared to be a relatively cost-effective intervention for improving health status among smokers although he recognized the imprecise and tentative nature of the results. He estimated that the cost (in 1985 UK prices) per quality adjusted life year of GP advice was £170 compared to approximately £1,700 for the alternative preventive interventions using drug therapy (hypertension control and serum cholesterol control). In comparison, Williams estimated an approximate cost per quality adjusted life year for common curative treatments for coronary heart disease such as coronary artery bypass grafting and heart transplants as being 20 to 40 times higher than that for GP advice to stop smoking. William's study provides tentative evidence that basic smoking cessation health education is a cost-effective use of resources compared to curative policies. Some adjustments were made to the assumptions used, for example predicting a lower quality adjusted life year outcome from smoking cessation due to the loss in satisfaction that may be experienced from actually stopping smoking. This, however, had little impact on the relative cost-effectiveness of the results.

In summary, the study by Williams provides a basic but informative illustration of a possible method for examining the relative cost-effectiveness of health education and health promotion interventions compared to a wide range of alternative health promoting or curative strategies.

Evaluation criteria applied to the smoking case studies

Scope

The assessment by Windsor, Warner and Cutter, (1988) of the relative cost-effectiveness of three alternative self-help methods for smoking cessation among pregnant smokers represented the most structured and detailed analysis of the studies reviewed. Cummings, Rubin and Oster (1989) and Williams (1987) used more general evaluations of the cost-effectiveness of smoking cessation health education, with both aiming to produce illustrative results that could be compared with cost-effectiveness estimates for a range of alternative preventive and curative strategies.

Generalizability

The use of a randomized control trial study design by Windsor, Warner and Cutter, (1988) enabled a detailed and reliable analysis of the attributability of each option to achieving end-of-pregnancy smoking cessation among women attending the pre-natal clinics (i.e. a high degree of internal validity). However, because of the necessarily small and focused scale of the evaluation, the generalizability of the findings to actual settings is limited. The study provides little insight into the cost-effectiveness of self-help health education options for pregnant smokers in other settings or guidance for the wider implementation of such strategies.

At the other extreme the generalizability of the findings in the studies by Williams (1987) and Cummings, Rubin and Oster (1989) is constrained by their lack of a structured study design and their extensive use of published data and assumptions about costs and outcomes. The external validity of their cost-effectiveness results could have been improved if actual data on costs and outcomes had been collected using a quasi-experimental study design. However, for a study to measure actual final health outcomes (as both Williams and Cummings, Rubin and Oster have attempted), it would require a study period that is beyond the scope of most research projects.

Comparability

Despite the greater reliability of the results produced by Windsor *et al.* (1988) it is difficult to compare the findings in this study with results from other studies. It is only possible to compare the these findings for cost-effectiveness with other studies of smoking cessation interventions aimed at pregnant women attending pre-natal clinics.

The main purpose of the approach adopted by Williams (1987) and Cummings, Rubin and Oster, (1989) is to enable wider comparisons of the relative cost-effectiveness of health education interventions and alternative health programmes and to assist priority setting in resource use. Their results demonstrate the potential application of health outcome measures, such as quality adjusted life years, for this purpose. However, there is a need for better data on quality of life outcomes and for more debate about the appropriateness of the current health status measures available before accurate statements on the cost-effectiveness of health education using such methods can be made.

9.5 Case study C – workplace health promotion

Several studies have been published in the US debating the economic costs and benefits of workplace health promotion. In the UK until recently less attention had been given to workplace health promotion, although the economic issues involved with this setting have recently been reviewed (Bovell, 1992). However, no published cost-effectiveness analyses of actual programmes could be found for the UK.

Most of the economic evaluations carried out in the US have been motivated by the notion that the main benefit of health promotion programmes in the workplace are the resource savings they can generate (Warner *et al.*, 1988). Many large companies in the US provide a company health insurance scheme for their employees. This has resulted in many private sector companies sponsoring the evaluation of the health promotion programmes they operate to determine their potential for producing cost savings for the company, in particular, by reducing the number of claims made on company health insurance policies.

Three typical business-orientated studies of workplace health promotion are reviewed in this case study section. They are assessed as a group because of close similarities in their objectives and methods of economic evaluation. Attention is focused on the use of the scope, generalizability and comparability and evaluation criteria to illustrate the fundamental flaws that exist in almost all workplace health promotion studies which have company cost savings as the main rationale for the intervention and the economic analysis.

The studies

1. Schwartz, R.M. and Rollins, P.L. (1985). Measuring the cost benefit of wellness strategies. *Business and Health*, October, pp. 24–6.
2. Gibbs, J.O., Mulvaney, D., Henes, C. *et al.* (1985). Worksite health promotion. Five-year trend in employee health care costs. *Journal of Occupational Medicine*, **27** (11), pp. 826–30.
3. Patterson, D. (1986). Determining cost benefits of worksite wellness. *Business and Health*, October, pp. 40–1.

Problem definition, objectives and options

The study problem in each study was to identify the short-term impact of health promotion programmes for employees on company costs accrued through health insurance claims. In each case the perspective adopted was that of the company. The objective was to identify the potential for the intervention to reduce short-term company health insurance claims, and to examine whether savings (benefits) accrued exceeded the costs of the health promotion programme. The Schwartz and Rollins (1985) study is the only one of the three which states that the health promotion programme being evaluated also had the aim of reducing absenteeism, increasing productivity, improving the well-being of employees and reducing the future incidence of major chronic disease (however, these objectives were not assessed in their paper).

Each of the three studies evaluated a multi-component company health promotion programme. Gibbs et al. (1985) assessed the Blue Cross and Blue Shield of Indiana employee health promotion programme which offered health checks, health education on risk behaviour and group programmes on nutrition, weight reduction, smoking cessation and exercise. Schwartz and Rollins (1985) evaluated a health enhancement programme offered to employees of the Atlantic Richfield Company, which covered smoking cessation and colorectal cancer education, screening for hypertension and breast self-examination for cancer. The company health promotion programme assessed by Patterson (1986) was centred around the provision of a facility for sessions on weight control and nutrition, exercise and fitness, stress management, smoking cessation, health checks and accident prevention.

Study design

Two of the studies set up structured study designs in an attempt to provide scientific validity to the effectiveness evaluation. Gibbs et al. (1985) randomly allocated 1,400 employees of their study company to a health promotion intervention group and a 'no programme' control group. Each group received general health education material, but employees in the intervention group also attended health risk screening and all those identified as at-risk of ill health attended appropriate health promotion sessions. Patterson (1986) used a quasi-experimental design in assigning employees of the study company to a 'health promotion' group and 'no-health promotion' control according to a prior 'needs assessment' exercise. A total of 238 employees in each group were matched for age and sex. In both studies the health insurance claims of the intervention and control groups were compared over an 18-month to four-year period.

An assessment of the wider social and economic benefits of a workplace health promotion intervention was attempted by Schwartz and Rollins (1985) although a less rigorous non-experimental design was used for this purpose. In this study the hypothetical impact of a company health promotion programme on annual medical treatment and care, short and long run disability payments, excess absenteeism and permanent replacement costs was estimated for a cohort of 39,000 employees in 1982.

Costs and outcomes

The calculation of costs and benefits was poorly undertaken in all three studies. Gibbs *et al.* (1985) and Patterson (1986) included only the direct costs to the employer of the intervention and provided no information on how they derived the cost estimate (only a single estimate was provided). The 'cost-benefit analysis' of Schwartz and Rollins did not even include an assessment of the costs of the health promotion programme to set against the potential cost savings.

Outcomes were simply measured as the difference in annual health insurance claim costs between programme and no-programme recipients in the studies of Gibbs *et al.* (1985) and Patterson (1986). In the study by Schwartz and Rollins (1985), outcomes were measured in terms of potential medical related savings and productivity gains. The authors arbitrarily assumed a 50% reduction in coronary heart disease risk from eliminating hypertension problems and unrealistically assumed 100% effectiveness in achieving smoking cessation, 100% success in identifying early breast cancer through screening and the achievement of the complete prevention of colorectal cancer in the workplace.

Results

Given the deficiencies in measurements of costs and outcomes in the studies the results they produce are likely to be imprecise and potentially misleading. Unfortunately, each study has attempted to provide a definitive figure to demonstrate the cost-effectiveness of workplace health promotion when a range of estimates would have been more appropriate.

Gibbs *et al.* (1985) found that participants of the health promotion programme incurred higher health care costs than non-participants in the first six months of the intervention, but over five years participants' costs were 24% lower. The intervention was judged to be cost-effective as the total cost savings exceeded initial programme costs by a factor of 1.45. Patterson (1986) claimed that the ratio of benefits to costs of health promotion was in the order of 2.2:1. In contrast, the potential cost savings to the company from a health promotion programme were estimated by Schwartz and Rollins at approximately US$55 million per annum, although the length of time for which such savings were likely was not specified in the paper.

Evaluation criteria

The main deficiencies in previous economic evaluations of workplace health promotion in the US can be identified by applying the scope, generalizability and comparability criteria.

Scope

The options assessed in most workplace evaluations have in general been multi-component programmes with interventions covering an array of health education, secondary prevention, health support and preventive drug therapy measures. For example, Warner *et al.* (1988) defined several areas of health promotion activity in a review of 400 financial and economic evaluations of workplace interventions. These covered behavioural change measures such as smoking cessation, nutrition and weight loss, exercise, stress reduction and health risk appraisal programmes, health support measures such as no-smoking policies, and secondary prevention hypertension control programmes.

The focus in many evaluations has been on the overall impact on company costs of behavioural change such as smoking cessation with little attempt to assess the relative cost-effectiveness of alternative health promotion strategies for achieving this objective.

Generalizability

The generalizability to actual settings of results from previous workplace health promotion evaluations has been limited by the restricted perspective adopted. Most studies with experimental study designs have collected data from one company and assessed the net financial cost impact of a health promotion intervention on that enterprise alone. The studies have generally been motivated by the potential for health promotion to achieve short-term (i.e. up to five years) profit gains. Warner *et al.* (1988) claimed this approach was fundamentally flawed, for two main reasons. Firstly, the potential increase in occupational pension payments and future health care costs if people live longer as a result of workplace health promotion are generally ignored. Secondly, several technical flaws exist, in particular most studies have very optimistic projections of programme effectiveness and total benefits. Often no allowance is made for the time lag between behavioural change and ill health risk reduction, and most lack an explicit consideration of the timing of costs and benefits by simply summing them regardless of when they are actually incurred.

A survey of 550 US corporations operating health promotion programmes found that only 31 had evaluated the effectiveness or cost-effectiveness of their programme (Katzman and Smith, 1989). This study reported that health promotion programmes were being justified by companies on the grounds that they were good for staff morale and corporate image. However, the survey also found that such companies tended to consider health promotion programmes as one of the first areas in which to make financial cut-backs in times of recession.

The implication from reviews of workplace health promotion is that companies will only sponsor evaluations of the cost-effectiveness of such programmes they operate in order to identify cost savings and not if the main aim is to promote corporate image or promote staff well-being. A possible solution to this problem is to broaden the perspective of the evaluation of workplace health promotion strategies. This possibility exists for any new UK studies that are conducted. The cost savings argument has only been developed in the US and does not transfer well to the UK context, as in the latter there is less reliance on company health insurance schemes paying for medical treatment and care.

In the UK scope exists for the government and other non-commercial agencies to fund economic evaluations of the cost-effectiveness of workplace health promotion from a social perspective, focusing on the costs and benefits to both employees and the companies involved. Close attention could then be given to the use of an appropriate study design to enable generalizability of the results in a UK context. Currently, the results from the US studies, even if they had been well designed, have very little bearing on predicting the potential cost-effectiveness of workplace health promotion in the UK. All that can be said from the US studies is that, in general, in the US context and from a single large company perspective, health promotion in the workplace may result in short-term financial savings. The evidence is insufficient to be a proven effect or to give any idea of the potential benefits to society.

Comparability

As most of the cost-benefit analyses of workplace health promotion conducted in the US have assessed the potential for short-term cost savings from the company perspective there appears to be some scope for comparisons of the results produced. For example, the benefits to costs ratios produced in the studies of Gibbs *et al.* (1985) and Patterson (1986) reviewed above could, in principle, be compared. In practice, differences between the studies in the specific methods used to calculate costs and benefits limits the value of making such comparisons. The danger is that misleading interpretations of the results might occur from any comparisons unless an appropriate framework for economic evaluation has been applied.

In conclusion, several reasons can be offered as to why the workplace provides a good setting for effective health promotion to achieve behavioural change – ease of access to a large group of people, the minimal cost to employees of participating, the existence of existing communication channels and facilities, administrative efficiency and the stability of the target population (Warner *et al.* 1988; Fielding 1990). Despite these advantages there has been a lack of evaluation of the cost-effectiveness of workplace health education and health promotion initiatives for achieving behavioural change. Instead most studies have focused on the final impact of behavioural change using arbitrary assumptions of the intermediate effectiveness of health promotion in the workplace. Warner *et al.* (1988) have argued that whilst there is a dearth of good information on cost-effectiveness, claims from studies of the economic merits of workplace health promotion should be greeted with a 'healthy scepticism'.

10 Future stages

The main purpose of this report has been to outline the methodological framework for undertaking a cost-effectiveness analysis of alternative health promotion interventions. The framework has been developed with the primary objective of assessing efficiency in health promotion. The aim has been to demonstrate the stages in the production of comparable cost-effectiveness results for a range of options.

The next stage in the development of the economic evaluation framework is to apply it to the assessment of the cost-effectiveness of actual health education and health promotion interventions. The first step in this process has been undertaken in chapter 9 of this report. This was to apply the framework to assessment of case studies of the cost-effectiveness of health promotion interventions. This exercise has demonstrated the limited scope of the economic evaluation of health promotion. For example, there has been very little economic evaluation of mass media-based health education, although several effectiveness studies have been undertaken. In addition, none of the community-based heart disease interventions have attempted to assess the cost-effectiveness of their component parts. Russell (1987b) has provided a review of the work on cost-effectiveness related to health promotion and prevention, and demonstrated its narrow focus.

The economic evaluations that have been done are also limited in terms of their generalizability and comparability. This is because of significant differences in the study design, cost and outcome measurements used in these studies. In addition, virtually all the cost-effectiveness results have been produced for the US, with limited relevance for the UK context.

The economic evaluation framework is being applied to the assessment of the UK Health Education Authority's programmes such as Look After Your Heart. The purpose of this is to examine the applicability of the framework for evaluating the cost-effectiveness of actual health promotion interventions. A further development of the framework would be to apply it as part of carefully designed projects for the analysis of the cost-effectiveness of alternative national and local health education interventions.

REFERENCES

Akehurst, R., Godfrey, C., Hutton, J. and Robertson, E. (1991). 'The Health of the Nation'. An economic perspective on target setting, Discussion Paper 92. Centre for Health Economics, University of York.

Altman, D. G. (1986). A framework for evaluating community based heart disease prevention programs. *Social Science and Medicine*, **22** (4), 479–87.

Baric, L. C. (1985). The meaning of words: health promotion. *The Journal of the Institute of Health Education*, **23** (1), 10–15.

Bergner, M., Bobbitt, R. A. and Kressel, S. (1981). The sickness impact profile. Development and final revision of a health status measure. *Medical Care*, **19**, 787–805.

Berwick, D. M., Cretin, S. and Keeler, E. (1981). Cholesterol, children and heart disease: an analysis of alternatives. *Pediatrics*, **68** (5), 721–30.

Bjorkquist, S., Tuomilehto, J., Puska, P. *et al.* (1979). Costs of hypertension programme of the North Karelia Project. In *Essential Hypertension*, ed. R. Thurm, Year Book Medical Publishers, Chicago.

Bovell, V. (1992). *Economic evaluation of workplace health promotion – an exploration of some of the principles involved*, MSc Dissertation, University of York.

Browner, W. S., Townsend, A. G., Duchene, A. G. and Hilley, S. B. (1990). Impact of the multiple risk factor intervention trial (MRFIT) smoking cessation programme on pulmonary function: a randomised control trial. *Clinical Research*, **8** (2).

Bush, J. W., Chen, M. and Patrick, D. L. (1973). Cost-effectiveness using a health status index: analysis of the New York State PKU screening program. In *Health Status Indexes*, ed. R. Berg. Hospital Research and Educational Trust, Chicago.

Cairns, J. (1991). *Health, Wealth and Time Preference*. Health Economics Research Unit Discussion Paper 07/91, University of Aberdeen.

Carr-Hill, R. A. (1989). Assumptions of the QALY procedure. *Social Science and Medicine*, **28**, 469–77.

Carr-Hill, R. A. (1992). Health related quality of life measurement – Euro style. *Health Policy*, **20**, 321–8.

Centers for Disease Control (1990). Healthy people 2000: national health promotion, disease prevention objectives for the year 2000. *Journal of the American Medical Association*, **264**, (16), 2057–60.

Cochrane, A. L. (1972). *Effectiveness and Efficiency: Random Reflections on Health Services*. Nuffield Provincial Hospitals Trust, London.

Cohen, D. R. and Henderson, J. B. (1988). *Health, Prevention and Economics*. Oxford University Press, London.

Collins, L. (1984). Concepts of health education: a study of four professional groups. *Journal of the Institute of Health Education*, **22**, (3), 81–8.

Coyle, D. and Tolley, K. (1992). *The discounting of health benefits in the pharmaco-economic analysis of drug therapies: an issue for debate? PharmacoEconomics*, Vol 2, No 2, 153–62.

Cribb, A. and Haycox A (1989). Economic analysis in evaluation of health promotion. *Community Medicine*, **11**, (4), 299–305.

Culyer, A. J. (1980). *The Political Economy of Social Policy*. Martin Robertson, Oxford.

Cummings, S. R., Rubin, S. M. and Oster, G. (1989). The cost-effectiveness of counselling smokers to quit. *Journal of the American Medical Association*, **261**, (1), 75–9.

Dawber, T. R. (1980). *The Framingham Study: the Epidemiology of Atherosclerotic Disease*. Havard University Press, Cambridge, Massachusetts.

Department of Health and Social Security (1977). *Priorities in the Health and Personal Social Services: The Way Forward*. HMSO, London.

Department of Health and Social Security (1979). *Prevention and Health: Everybody's Business*. HMSO, London.

Department of Health (1991). *The Health of the Nation: A Consultative Document for Health in England*. HMSO, London.

Department of Health (1992). *The Health of the Nation: A Strategy for Health in England*. HMSO, London.

Donaldson, C. and Russell, I. (1991). Ceteris Paribus? Study design in the economic evaluation of health care. *Paper presented to the Health Economists Study Group*, University of Aberdeen, July 1991.

Downie, R. S., Fyfe, C. and Tannahill, A. (1991). *Health Promotion: Models and Values*, Oxford University Press, Oxford.

Drummond, M. F. (1981). Studies in Economic Appraisal in Health Care. Oxford University Press, Oxford.

Drummond, M. (1989). Output measurement for resource allocation decisions in health care. *Oxford Review of Economic Policy*, **5** (1), 59–74.

Drummond, M. F., Ludbrook, A., Lowson, K. and Steele, A. (1987). *Studies in Economic Appraisal in Health Care*, vol. 2. Oxford University Press, Oxford.

Drummond, M. F., Stoddart, G. L. and Torrance, G. W. (1987). *Methods for the Economic Evaluation of Health Care Programmes*. Oxford University Press, Oxford.

Duncan, C., Stein, M. J. and Cummings, S. R. (1991). Staff involvement and special follow-up time increase physicians' counselling about smoking cessation: a controlled trial. *American Journal of Public Health*, **81** (7), 899–901.

Elixhauser, A. (1990). The costs of smoking and the cost-effectiveness of smoking cessation programs. *Journal of Public Health Policy*, Summer.

Engleman, S. R. and Forbes, J. F. (1986). Economic aspects of health education. *Social Science and Medicine*, **22** (4), 443–58.

EuroQol Group (1990). EuroQol – a new facility for the measurement of health related quality of life. *Health Policy*, **16**, 199–208.

Farquhar, J. W., Fortmann, S. P., Flora, J. A. *et al.* (1990). Effects of community wide education on cardiovascular disease risk factor. The Stanford five-city project. *Journal of the American Medical Association*, **264**, 3, 359–65.

Fielding, J. E. (1990). Worksite health promotion programs in the United States: progress, lessons and challenges. *Health Promotion International*, **5**, (1), 75–84.

Flay, B. R. (1986). Efficacy and effectiveness trials (and other phases of research) in the development of health promotion programs. *Preventive Medicine*, **15**, 451–74.

Gibbs, J. O., Mulvaney, D., Henes, C. *et al.* (1985). Work-site health promotion. Five-year trend in employee health care costs. *Journal of Occupational Medicine*, **27** (11), 826–30.

Godfrey, C., Hardman, G. and Tolley, K. (1992). *Cost-Effectiveness of Health Promotion: Application to Coronary Heart Disease*, Centre for Health Economics, University of York.

Green, L. W. (1979). How to evaluate health promotion. *Hospitals*, Oct 1st 1979.

Green, L. W. (1984). Modifying and developing health behaviour. *Annual Review of Public Health*, **5**, 215–36.

Green, L. W., Kreuter, M. W., Deeds, S. G. and Partridge, K. (1980). *Health Education Planning: A Diagnostic Approach*. Mayfield, Palo Alto.

Gunning-Schepers, L. (1989). The health benefits of prevention – a simulation approach. *Health Policy Special Issue*, **12** (1–2).

Hatziandreu, E. I., Koplan, J. P., Weinstein, M. C. *et al*. (1988). A cost-effectiveness analysis of exercise as a health promotion activity. *American Journal of Public Health*, **78** (11), 1417–21.

Health Promotion Authority for Wales (1990). *Health for All in Wales*, Part B, Health Promotion Authority for Wales.

Hetzel, B. S. and Berenson, G. S. (1987). *Cardiovascular Risk Factors in Childhood: Epidemiology and Prevention*. Elsevier Science Publishers, New York.

Higgins, C. W. (1988). The economics of health promotion. *Health Values*, **12** (5), 39–45.

Holland, W. W. and Stewart, S. (1991). *Screening in Health Care. Benefit or Bane?* The Nuffield Provincial Hospitals Trust, London.

Hunt, S., McKenna, S., McEwan, J. *et al*. (1980). A quantitative approach to perceived health status: a validation study. *Journal of Epidemiology and Community Health*, **34**, 281–6.

Kaplan, R. M. (1988). New health promotion indicators: the general health policy model. *Health Promotion*, **3** (1), 35–50.

Kaplan, R. M. and Anderson, J. P. (1988). The quality of well-being scale: rationale for a single quality of life index. In *Quality of Life: Assessment and Application*, ed. S. R. Walker and R. Rosser, 51–77. MTP Press, London.

Kaplan, R. M., Atkins, C. J., and Wilson, D. K. (1988). The cost-utility of diet and exercise interventions in non-insulin dependent diabetes mellitus. *Health Promotion*, **2** (4), 331–40.

Katzman, M. S. and Smith, K. J. (1989). Occupational health promotion programs: evaluation efforts and measured cost savings. *Health Values*, **13** (2), 3–10.

Keeler, E. B., Manning, W. G., Newhouse, J. P. *et al*. (1989). The external costs of a sedentary lifestyle. *American Journal of Public Health*, **79** (8), 975–80.

Kickbush, I. (1989). Healthy cities: a working project and growing movement. *Health Promotion*, **4** (2), 77–82.

Kind, P. (1988). *The Design and Construction of Quality of Life Measures*. Discussion Paper 43, Centre for Health Economics, University of York.

Kind, P., Rosser, R. and Williams, A. (1982). Valuation of quality of life: some psychometric evidence. In *The Value of Life and Safety*, ed. M. W. Jones-Lee, North Holland Publishing Co, 159–70.

Koskela, K. and Puska, P. (1987). Community action against cardiovascular disease in Finland. *World Health Forum*, **8**, 53–5.

Kristein, M. M. (1977). Economic issues in prevention. *Preventive Medicine*, **6**, 252–64.

Liederkerken, P. C., Jonkers, R., de Haes, W. F. M. *et al*. (1990). *Effectiveness of Health Education*. Dutch Health Education Centre, Utrecht, The Netherlands.

Loomes, G. and McKenzie, L. (1989). The use of QALYs in health care decision making, *Social Science and Medicine*, **28** (4), 299–308.

Milio, N. (1990). Healthy cities: the new public health and supportive research. *Health Promotion International*, **5** (4), 291–7.

Mittlemark, M. B., Leupher, R. V., Grimm, R. *et al*. (1988). The role of physicians in a community wide program for the prevention of cardiovascular disease: the Minnesota Heart Health Program. *Public Health Reports*, **103** (4), 360–65.

Mooney, G. (1983). Equity in health care: confronting the confusion. *Effective Health Care*, **1**, 179–85.

Nutbeam, D. (1986). Health promotion glossary. *Health Promotion*, **1**, 113–27.

Nutbeam, D. and Catford, J. (1987). The Welsh Heart Program evaluation strategy: progress, plans and possibilities. *Health Promotion*, **2** (1), 5–18.

Nutbeam, D., Smith, C. and Catford, J. (1990). Evaluation in health education. A review of progress, possibilities and problems. *Journal of Epidemiology and Community Health*, **44**, 83–9.

Ottawa Charter for Health Promotion (10986). *Health Promotion*, **1** (4), iii–iv.

Parsonage, M. and Neuberger, H. (1992). Discounting and health benefits. *Health Economics*, **1**, 71–6.

Patterson, D. (1986). Determining cost benefits of worksite wellness. *Business and Health*, October, 40–1.

Pocock, S. J. and Thompson, S. G. (1990). Primary prevention trials in cardiovascular disease. *Journal of Epidemiology and Community Health*, **44**, 3–6.

Reid, D. and Smith, N. (1990). What is the single most important intervention for the prevention of smoking related disease? *Proceedings of the 7th World Conference on Tobacco and Health*, Perth, Western Australia; Department of Health.

Reid, D., Killoran, A., McNeill, A. and Chambers, J. (1992). Choosing the most effective health promotion options for reducing a nation's smoking prevalence. *Tobacco Control*, **1**, 185–97.

Robine, J. M. and Ritchie, K. (1991). Healthy life expectancy: evaluation of global indicator of change in population health. *British Medical Journal*, **302**, 457–60.

Rogers, P. J., Eaton, E. K. and Bruhn, J. G. (1981). Is health promotion cost-effective? *Preventive Medicine*, **10**, 324–39.

Russell, L. B. (1984). The economics of prevention. *Health Policy*, **4**, 85–100.

Russell, L. B. (1986). *Is Prevention Better Than Cure?* Brookings Institution, Washington DC.

Russell, L. B. (1987a). The economics of prevention: a reply to Roy Shephard. *Health Policy*, **7**, 57–9.

Russell, L. B. (1987b). *Evaluating Preventive Care. Report on a Workshop.* Brookings Institute, Washington DC.

Schaapveld, K., Bergsma, E. W., van Ginneken, J. S. *et al.* (1990). *Setting Priorities in Prevention.* TNO Institute for Preventive Health Care, The Netherlands.

Schwartz, R. M. and Rollins, P. L. (1985). Measuring the cost-benefit of wellness strategies. *Business and Health*, October, 24–6.

Scottish Home and Health Department (1991). *Health Education in Scotland: A National Policy Statement*, Edinburgh.

Shephard, R. J. (1985). The impact of exercise upon medical costs. *Sports Medicine*, **2**, 133–43.

Shephard, R. J. (1987). The economics of prevention: a critique. *Health Policy*, **7**, 49–56.

Simons-Morton, B. G., Parcel, G. S., Baranowski, T. *et al.* (1991). Promoting physical activity and a healthful diet among children: results of a school-based intervention study. *American Journal of Public Health*, **81**, 886–91.

St Leger, A. S. (1989). Would a healthier population consume fewer health service resources? A life table analysis using hospital in-patient enquiry bed-usage statistics as a proxy for hospital treatment costs. *International Journal of Epidemiology*, **18** (1), 227–31.

Sullivan, D. F. (1971). A single index of mortality and morbidity. *Health Services and Mental Health Administration Health Reports*, **86**, 347–54.

Tannahill, A (1985). What is health promotion? *Health Education Journal*, **44** (4), 167–8.

Toevs, C. D., Kaplan, R. M. and Atkins, C. J. (1984). The costs and effects of behavioural programs in chronic obstructive pulmonary disease. *Medical Care*, **22** (12), 1088–99.

Tolley, K. and Rowland, N. (1991). Identification of alcohol-related problems in a general hospital setting – a cost-effectiveness evaluation. *British Journal of Addiction*, **86**, 429–38.

Tones, K. (1983). Education and Health Promotion: new direction. *The Journal of the Institute of Health Education*, **21** 121–31.

Tones, K. (1990). *The power to choose: health education and the new public health*, Health Education Unit, Leeds Polytechnic, UK.

U.S. Department of Health, Education and Welfare (DHEW), Public Health Service (1979) *Healthy People: The Surgeon-General's Report on health promotion and disease prevention*, DHEW Publication (PHS) 79-55071, Washington DC, USA.

Vuori, H. (1979). The medical model and the objectives of health education, *Paper presented at the XIth International Conference on Health Education*, London.

Warner, K. E. (1979). The economic implications of preventive health care. *Social Science and Medicine*, **13**C, 227–37.

Warner, K. E. (1987). Health and economic implications of tobacco-free society. *Journal of the American Medical Association*, **258** (15), 2080–6.

Warner, K. E., Wickizer, T. M., Wolfe, R. A. *et al.*, (1988). Economic implications of workplace health promotion programs: review of the literature. *Journal of Occupational Medicine*, **30** (2), 106–12.

Weinkam, J. J. Rosenbaum, W. and Sterling, T. D. (1987). Smoking and hospital utilisation. *Social Science and Medicine*, **24** (11), 983–6.

Wellings, K. and McVey, D. (1990). Evaluation of the HEA AIDS press campaign: December 1988 to March 1989. *Health Education Journal*, **49** (3), 108–16.

Whitehead, M. and Dahlgren, G. (1991). What can be done about inequalities in health? *The Lancet*, **338**, 1059–63.

Williams, A. (1987). Screening for risk of CHD: Is it a wise use of resources? In *Screening for Risk of Coronary Heart Disease*, ed. M. Oliver. John Wiley & Sons, London.

Windsor, R. A., Warner, K. E. and Cutter, G. R. (1988). A cost-effectiveness analysis of self-effectiveness analysis of self help smoking cessation methods for pregnant women. *Public Health Reports*, **103** (1), 83–8.

World Health Organization (1985). Health Promotion. *The Journal of the Institute of Health Education*, **23** (1), 5–9.

World Health Organization (1990). Prevention in childhood and youth of adult cardiovascular diseases: time for action. *Report of a WHO expert committee*, WHO, Geneva.